THE FORMATION OF
MODERN OBJECTIVITY

DAVID CASTILLEJO

THE FORMATION OF
MODERN OBJECTIVITY

EDICIONES DE ARTE Y BIBLIOFILIA. MADRID

EDICIONES DE ARTE Y BIBLIOFILIA
Calle Ponzano, 69. Tels.: 442 43 39 y 442 51 78. Madrid-3
ISBN: 84-85005-61-9. Depósito legal: M. 36474-1982

While working on the material for this book I was greatly helped by seven people. Walter Strich taught me how to think, Frances Cornford taught me how to write, Morgan Forster taught me how to construct, Gwen Raverat taught me how to be truthful, my mother taught me psychology, and Lydia Keynes taught me about gaiety. The work itself owes most to Walter Strich, who, in weekly conversations over four years, gave me a wider vision of culture and philosophy than I could even absorb or understand at the time. But the book would never have been written without the help of John Nye. When I had completely lost heart it was he who insisted that I write it, and he went patiently through my hopelessly jumbled first draft, paragraph by paragraph, and guided me with his careful mind. So I dedicate this work to all my helpers, and especially to him.

DAVID CASTILLEJO

CONTENTS

CHAPTER I

THE MEDIEVAL COSMOS

If we try to understand any past cosmology by comparing it to our own, we must either assume that the history of thought is one long process of gradual approximation to the truth, and the past a series of diminishing mistakes; or else we must assume that different ages have had different patterns of thought and different systems of reality, and ours is only one of these.

The second alternative is by far the more interesting because we then come straight up against the functioning of relativism: there is no absolute point of reference, say present-day knowledge, from which we can understand or judge past systems of thought; and there is no common mould of language by which to explain a past idea, since even language changes meaning down the ages.

This is apparently a fact, key words have changed their meaning with time, more than has been reckoned for, and to an extent that makes much of our understanding of past thought a rather pathetic conjecture.

To illustrate this I shall give here a broad resumé of medieval cosmology, and show how it differs in almost every respect from modern thought. I shall then describe how it went through various stages of change before it reached the modern cosmology that we are familiar with.

*   *   *

Unlike the modern world, the medieval cosmos has two separate levels of reality. Above us is the heavenly world in which the stars, sun and planets revolve in their crystal spheres. The outermost revolving sphere is a *primum mobile* which gives its motion to the blue firmament with its fixed stars. This firmament makes a complete revolution every twenty four hours and carries along with it all the other spheres within it. Inside this firmament is the sphere of Saturn that lags behind, or else has a retrograde motion of its own taking thirty years to complete. Inside that is the sphere of Jupiter, then the sphere of Mars, then that of the Sun (which takes one year to complete its retrograde motion in respect of the stars), then that of Venus, then of Mercury, and finally the sphere of the Moon, which completes its retrograde motion in one month. This celestial world is immutable and perfect. The material of which it is made is variously described as crystal, or a pure quintessence, and it is subtle, simple and clear. This world is heavenly in a theological sense, and is close to divinity. It is peopled by angels.

Below this lies the elemental reality in which we live. This also contains its spheres or regions, rather like the rings of an onion, and these hold the four elements, each

8

in its own region; but the four elements do not revolve. The outermost region, nearest the moon, is the region of fire. We cannot see this fire when we look up because it is pure and uncontaminated with earthly dross. But all disturbances such as comets and shooting stars that appear to take place in heaven are in fact occurring in this lower region of fire.

Below fire is the sphere of air, which is sometimes described as having three layers — the middle layer being that of the clouds. Below this, at the very centre of the world, are water and earth. These are mixed up in seas and continents, but earth tends to fall below water, and is said to belong at the centre or lowest part of the world.

All the objects of this 'sublunary' world are composed of these four elements of fire, air, water and earth, and the various changing proportion and antagonisms between the elements cause the change and corruption of sublunary things.

There are two kinds of motion in the cosmos: circular motion which is natural to the heavens, and motion in a straight line which is natural to the elements. The elements of fire and air have the property of levity and tend to move up towards the circumference of the world; water and earth are heavy and tend to move down towards the centre of the world. Each element has an 'appetite' to reach its natural place.

However, below these two great regions of the world, or rather hidden secretly inside every object, there is a

9

third order of being called 'matter'. Matter cannot be perceived. The only thing that can be seen is form. Matter is like a dark and formless mud, synonymous with potentiality, and has the seed of different forms within it. Matter is constantly pushing itself up in an effort to reach a stable and complete form. This appetite of matter for form is really the force that causes growth and change.

Only the elemental part of the world has matter, constantly disturbing its equilibrium. The heavenly world has no matter in it. It is pure form. Only the elemental world is subject to procreation and corruption; the heavenly world is unchanging and stable.

The cosmos therefore resembles an onion with concentric rings one inside the other, the outer set of rings revolving and composed of the heavens, and the inner set of rings static but disturbed, and composed of the elements.

There are two contrary cosmic forces at work on the elemental part of the world: the rays of influence which the planets, stars and signs of the zodiac radiate down towards the earth; and the power of matter which is struggling upward towards pure form.

Each planet and sign of the zodiac is closely allied to one or more of the elements, and each has a character and personality of its own — akin to the personality of the god or beast after which it is named. The planets especially are vast personalities radiating their influence into all the regions of the vegetable, animal and mineral world.

Man stands in the centre of this cosmos. He is a microcosm or 'small world' reflecting within himself the whole structure of the macrocosm or 'great world'. The four elements cause his varying temperament: flegmatic, choleric, melancholic or sanguine. Likewise all the other cosmic forces and events are reflected in him. The struggle of matter to reach a stable form is akin to his own struggle to reach the purity and harmony of the heavens.

Motion in the medieval world is of two kinds: it is either *natural* and inherent in the body, like the growth of a plant towards its complete form, and the motion of different objects towards their natural cosmic region; or else it is *violent* and accidental and exerted from the outside, as when one body pushes another or when one element harms another. Natural motion is the more important; violent motion is of relatively small significance, except that it causes suffering and disease, and disturbs natural order.

There are three words to describe place. The whole world is visualised as a solid body, where everything has its own natural place, its *locus*. When any object moves, its vacated place is immediately filled by another object, because there is no such thing as emptiness in this world, there is no *vacuum*. However, there is also an unimportant little word *spatium* of almost no significance, which merely means the interval or distance between two objects.

*   *   *

This medieval world was built up slowly during the Middle Ages from information given in the Bible, Plato's *Timaeus,* Aristotle's physical works, and Ptolemy's astronomy.

The inconsistencies and contradictions between one classical author and another did not greatly trouble medieval thinkers. They used the authority of whichever author was most relevant for each occasion. Aristotle had said that the heavenly planets revolve in solid crystal spheres. Ptolemy, however, working out the exact path of the planets, found it necessary to imagine the existence of small epicycles in which each planet was revolving on an axis of its own within the solid body of its own cosmic sphere, thus damaging the simplicity of the crystal spheres. These epicycles explained the erratic advancing and retrograde steps which each planet was seen to take [1]. Ptolemy's theory really invalidates Aristotle's physics, but both theories were allowed to exist side by side. Ptolemy was used when the motion

---

[1] We can understand this better if we imagine a fly walking round in a circle on a table. Placing your eye at the level of the table, the fly will appear simply to be moving backwards and forwards. In this way Ptolemy's small epicycles were devised to explain the apparently erratic advancing and retrograde steps of the planets.

12

of the planets had to be plotted, and Aristotle was referred to when the physical nature of the heavens was being
discussed.

The same duplicity of view-points occurred when Copernicus first put forward his astronomical theory. The
Church agreed that his method of calculating with an
earth moving round the sun simplified the mathematics,
and could therefore be used for calculations; but the
'physical truth' nevertheless was as Aristotle had said,
that the sun moves round the earth and the earth is at
the centre of the world.

By the time printing started up in the fifteenth century,
there was already a considerable literature on cosmology,
and the patterns of thought were fairly fixed. Any educated reader would be expected, for example, to understand the following passage, a description of the way
matter works its way up towards perfect *form* by swinging
itself between the cosmic opposites of heat, cold, dry and
moist:

> In matter there is hidden a sort of active might, that
> is a sort of imperfect form: and this might is common
> to two contraries. Therefore when that might is
> brought to act, and hath taken shape, he immediately
> has appetite to be under a contrary shape. As this
> might is indifferent to heat and to cold, when he had
> indeed received heat, he immediately has an appetite
> to receive the contrary. And so no forms of things
> that are corruptible and generable, may sufficiently
> and at full have active power over matter. But it

13

always has an appetite to be fulfilled by another shape[...] so it excites the active form to a contrary form; and gives to it some more perfect being, till it be under the most perfect being of form [2].

This passage is profoundly difficult for a modern reader to understand. However, the following description of how the great *macrocosm* influences man the *microcosm,* will be more familiar to us. It is remarkable how far the mercurial influence was thought to spread. *The Shepherd's Kalendar* tells us that the man born under Mercury

shall get many friends and lovers with his wisdom and labour; he resorts to those of good manners, is fortunate on the sea and in merchandise, is very gracious; shall have harm of women, when he is married men will respect him less, he will love women greatly but they will never master him; he will be a good man of the church; hate going to war, hate thieves and swearers, get great goods by his wisdom; he will be good in some craft; he will love to preach and speak rhetoric and talk Philosophy and Geometry, will have love of writing and will read strange books and cast accounts and numbers, a maker of songs ballads and rhymes, perfect in music and will love it; will be a

---

[2] Taken from the text in 'Batman upon Bartholomew, his Book De Proprietatibus Rerum' London 1582, p. 153. From internal evidence it seems that the book was originally written about 1250. See the *Dictionary of National Biography,* under Glanville, Bartholomew de.

14

great clothmaker, have love of measuring; be the servant of some great lord, receiver of his money; will have a fair forehead, a long visage, black eyes, a thin beard, and be a great pleader in the law, and he will meddle with other men's deeds if they do not well, and say against it. And Mercury governs the thighs, flanks and belly [3].

This passage is familiar to us because the dramatists of the sixteenth and seventeenth centuries popularised the temperamental nature of man — watch Mercutio in *Romeo and Juliet*. And because astrology is still popular.

*   *   *

STRUCTURAL ANALYSIS

Was this medieval world just a medley of theories culled from the Greeks and put together to fit into a more or less satisfactory pattern, only to fall to pieces again when it was questioned in the seventeenth century? No, curiously enough medieval cosmology has a high-powered consistency of its own. The whole world, and everything in it, is an *internal division of totality*.

These three concepts *totality*, *internal* and *division* are foreign to modern scientific thought, and we must therefore approach them very delicately.

---

[3] *The Shepherd's Kalendar*, London, 1656, p. M3. First published in Paris in 1493, its astrological passages derive from earlier sources.

15

Our modern physical world is made up of objects and forces in space, but at no point does modern thought stipulate an idea of totality. The most that is envisaged today is an indefinite number of particles, or an indefinitely extended space. There is also no distinction in modern science between internal and external qualities. In a field of indefinitely extended space everything is in a sense *external*, and the parts are externally related to each other and can be analysed into any number of external sub-divisions.

Furthermore, in modern reality any object can be analysed down to its smallest particles, but this is only a quantitative or numerical division. Modern scientific thought does not have the concept of division in the medieval sense, which is *division into opposites* in *qualitative* stages. Medieval opposites are alien to modern science. In a sense, of course, a modern acid and an alkali can be termed opposite because they are chemically operative on each other, and a positive and negative electric charge could be called opposite. But this is not the sense of medieval opposites, which are internal divisions at a cosmic level.

The structure of the medieval cosmos, analysed out, is therefore as follows:

(i) *TOTALITY*. The world is a unity or totality in place, time and form. Outside the outermost sphere there is no place. The cosmos is spherical and can therefore revolve on itself without occupying any other place but itself. The cosmos finishes at the divine un-moved *prime mover* who moves the outermost sphere. There is no empty place outside. In the eighteenth century people wondered what they would meet if they stood on the edge of the world and put their hand out. But the eighteenth century had acquired a conception of extended space which the Middle Ages did not possess. The outermost part of the medieval world was so mysterious and divine that such a question could hardly have arisen.

Similarly the medieval cosmos is a temporal whole. It contains all time within it, from the first day of the Creation to the last Day of Judgment. Before the Creation and after the Day of Judgment there is no time, there is Eternity. And Eternity in the medieval sense does not mean an indefinite prolongation of time, it means time-lessness altogether.

Finally the structure of the cosmos is a totality because it is a sphere — and a sphere is the shape that contains the maximum volume. This unity or wholeness of the medieval world becomes even clearer from its internal structure.

(ii) *INTERNAL DIVISIONS.* The divisions inside the cosmos were created by God when he took undifferentiated matter and *divided out* the opposites. The Bible says that God divided the light from the darkness, and the land from the water. Medieval authors say that he also divided out the four elements mentioned by the Greeks.

Here is a description of the Creation by an alchemist, from a manuscript among Newton's alchemical papers. This description gives the Platonic theory that the Idea precedes the physical entity, followed by the Biblical division into opposites:

> When there was neither time nor place did God create a certain invisible chaos, invisible, intangible, which the Philosophers call Hyle or the most remote matter, out of this he made an extract or second matter or chaos which the philosophers do know, not by speculation but by sense; that matter was and is visible and tangible in which were and are all the seeds and forms of all the Creatures, superior and inferior that ever were made. From this God divided out the four elements and in a word did make all things celestial and terrestrial [1].

So by degrees of creation God first made a 'remote' matter, then a visible matter, and finally *divided* the elements out of this. Thus the four elements are internal divisions arising from this single material, and lie one stage ahead in degree of differentiation. Creation is achieved by this curious method of distinguishing or pulling out opposites which contrast with each other, and are yet in a sense dependent on each other for their quality, and remain cradled together inside a greater cosmic structure. Here is where opposites in the medieval sense differ from anything in modern science — and are more

---

[1] From the Keynes MS. 33 in King's College Cambridge, p. 2.

like some modern psychological concepts. The fire or water that a modern scientist deals with are not internal divisions of unity. In fact modern fire and water have no particular link with unity or totality and no special connection with it. It is a different system of relationships. So if we are going to define things by their *relationships*, we must say that modern fire and water have very different structures and relationships from Greek or medieval fire and water.

This concept of internal divisions radiating out from unity appears clearly in the medieval theory of number. Today we usually imagine numbers lying in a long line, rather as a string of beads, or equal measurements on a ruler. The Middle Ages had the idea that all number is an internal division of unity. Here is a 16th century popular account expressing the medieval view [5]:

> Mark here what Figure stands for One, the right
> Root of all Number; and of Infinity:
> Love's happiness, the praise of Harmony,
> Nursery of All, and end of Polymny;
> No Number, but more than a Number yet:
> Potentiality in all, and all in it.

The number One, or unity, is being described as the origin and nursery of everything, containing everything in it before the differentiation into parts.

---

[5] From *Du Bartas his Divine Weeks and Works*. Translated by J. Sylvester. 1621 edition, p. 288.

> Now note Two's character, One's heir apparent,
> As the first-born; first Number, and the Parent
> Of Female pairs.

So two is referred to as the first created number. This passage does not mention division into opposites, it only mentions the Pythagorean theory that even numbers are feminine.

> Here now observe the Three,
> Th'eldest of Odd, God's number properly;
> Wherein both Number and no-number enter;
> Heav'ns dearest Number, whose enclosed Centre
> Doth equally from both extremes extend:
> The first that hath beginning, midst and end.

Three is therefore the first odd number, since one is not strictly speaking a number but rather undifferentiated totality. Three is equated with the Trinity, and it is viewed as two extremes joining at the centre. Unity at an undifferentiated level is therefore everything, and no-number. But once internal divisions start, it becomes the centre or intermediary between two extremes, as well as the all-containing three-in-one of the Trinity. Three is the first fully created structure.

> The (Cubes-base) Four; a full and perfect sum,
> Whose added parts just unto Ten do come;
> Number of God's great name, Seasons, Complexions,
> Winds, Elements, and Cardinal Perfections.

Four reveals two sets of opposites radiating out, hence the four directions, and the four elements.

(iii) *CENTRALIZED PATTERNS.* Any radiating system of opposites implies a centralized pattern, and centrally constructed patterns appear in almost every branch of medieval thought. All the patterns tend to refer ultimately to the centralized structure of the cosmos itself, or to the Trinity.

The elemental opposites were divided out from an undifferentiated whole. Before the division there was no distinction between centre and extremes. After the division, as with the number three, the cosmos is created, and it has both a centre and a circumference. Its circumference shows that the cosmos is a whole; and its centre shows that it is centrally formed and internally constructed. Medieval thinkers all agreed that the earth is so small in relation to the world, that it is virtually only a point in comparison to it: but the earth is the central point of the whole cosmos.

Thus a circle with a point at the centre is almost a model of the medieval cosmos. Man lives at the centre of this cosmos, and he is a microcosm reflecting the whole cosmos in himself. I shall call this *pattern 1.*

However, in a sense all cosmic activity takes place between the two extremes of centre and circumference, and in this sense the centre lies half way between these extremes of up and down, and man is in the middle range. I shall call this *pattern 2.*

A good example of *pattern 2* appears in the medieval theory of natural elemental motion. According to medieval thought — following Aristotle — there are two types of motion in the cosmos: the circular motion of the heavens revolving on themselves; and the straight up and down motion of the elements between centre and circumference. Fire and water move naturally upwards, and water and earth naturally downwards. Medieval circular motion is what we today would call motion in space, and it does not constitue any change except change of place. However, medieval up and down motion involves a hierarchical or vertical change of quality, because anything that moves up or down shifts into a different sphere of the world, and changes its quality — either going up towards the heavens, or down towards dark undifferentiated matter.

air /

The medieval naming of dimensions illustrates this hieratic system. Whereas Euclid and modern thought say that the three dimensions are *breadth*, *height* and *length*, the medieval view is that the three dimensions correspond to the three natural motions, and are *breadth*, *height* and *depth*. Height and depth are spoken of as two separate dimensions because they constitute two opposite cosmic directions. They are not viewed as belonging to one continuum.

Here is an alchemist's description of the chaos, or original material on which the alchemist starts work. Notice the phrase 'as all things':

22

This Chaos as all things hath dimensions three
That is altitude, latitude and profundity[6].

The alchemist's chaos is a model not only of the whole cosmos, but of every single object. Sometimes these dimensions were combined with the Euclidean ones, and then we have four dimensions:

> Quadrate shape and square botokeneth[...] the steadfastness of a Christian soul in virtuous science and lore, that he knoweth with all Saints what is length and breadth, highness and deepness[7].

In so far as all activity is taking place between the centre and the circumference of the cosmos, man holds an intermediary position between these two extremes. This is his status in *pattern 2*. Matter lies below him, within him, or behind him, and pure form lies above him, or ahead of him.

The two cosmic directions of up and down are also at work in heat and cold, and in levity and gravity, because these are the properties of bodies that make them have an appetite to go in the two opposite cosmic directions.

It will seem obvious to us that these centralized medieval patterns tacitly assume the presence of man somewhere as an intermediary: a thing only moves up or down in relation to man; a thing is only hot or cold in

---

[6] By Bloomfield. In Keynes MS. 15. King's College Cambridge.
[7] *Batman upon Bartholomew*, p. 413.

relation to man's temperature. But to the medieval mind they were absolute qualities of body. In so far as man's presence was providing a pivot to all structures, the medieval mind was unaware of it. If man was seeing the world from his point of view, or projecting his presence into its structure, it was unconsciously done.

What I have called *pattern 1* is the grandest picture: man and the cosmos face each other like two mirrors. What I have called *pattern 2* is already a more self-conscious or related vision. Here man's position in the cosmos between the opposites is tacitly acknowledged.

(iv) *PARALLEL STRUCTURES AND CORRESPONDENCES.* Medieval thought is known to have had a complicated system of parallelism or correspondences whereby the major cosmic patterns, or facets of them, are reflected again and again in the vegetable, animal and mineral kingdoms. Parallelism occurs in almost any cosmology — it is a transferring of one type of relationship to all facets of existence. However, the parallelisms are more complicated than usual in medieval thought. By far the most complex of these patterns of correspondence occurs in alchemy, which is worth describing in some detail as an example of how the medieval mind worked.

Alchemists believed that the structure of metals corresponds to the structure of the world as a whole, and therefore also to the structure of Man as microcosm. They were mainly concerned with the seven planetary metals, lead (Saturn), tin (Jupiter), iron (Mars), gold (the sun), copper (Venus), mercury (Mercury), and silver (the moon). They believed that all these metals, except gold, are at different stages of unripeness or 'potentiality', and the material in all of them is striving towards the stability and perfection of gold. Gold does not rust nor tarnish, whereas other metals do. Metals tarnish because they are composed of unbalanced proportions of the four elements, and, as we have seen, matter struggling up below the elements towards form causes the metals to change and be unstable. Gold, however, is perfect like the heavens. Gold is like the man who has achieved spiritual salvation and physical health. Gold alone has all four elements perfectly balanced and united in one simple whole. Gold is stable like the heavenly quintessence (or *fifth* essence, of which the heavens were said to be composed), it does not tarnish and is untouched by the vicissitudes and encroachments of time.

And here is the parallel with man: Man's body and temperament are also composed of the four elements in unstable proportions. An excess or deficiency of one of the elements in his body will make a man ill, and its total destruction will kill him. Man's health is precarious, and at best he can only take medicines to counteract the excesses of heat, cold, dryness or moisture — and he is whole and healthy only when the elements in him are united in perfect balanced proportion.

It was believed that the baser metals tend to ripen towards gold in the bowels of the earth, and this is a slow process. The alchemist tried to do in his laboratory over a short period of time what nature is doing over the centuries: making gold by redeeming matter and giving it a pure and stable form — saving it, rather as Christ had saved man. The alchemist's task was a natural, and yet an unnatural one; he was very absorbed in the working of nature and in the salvation of metals.

Alchemy, as so much medieval thought, operated by reducing everything once again to the undifferentiated wholeness of the cosmos before it was divided out into parts, in order to discover again, within the undivided whole, the seed of a perfect creation, and then from this seed create the perfect body.

There are many alchemical theories as to how the work was to be done, but the general pattern was to reduce the base metals and the elements by liquifying them down to their original *matter*, and then at this undifferentiated level, where forms are interchangeable and metals can be 'trans-formed' into tone another, unite the opposites in perfect proportion and give birth to the new perfect Being. The process is like reversing the order of the Creation, purifying the base matter, and then forming the perfect Being or sequence in the laboratory, almost at a speeded up rate.

Different alchemists were interested in different aspects of the work. Some were mainly concerned with transforming or transmuting base metals into gold. Others were interested in finding the seed of gold, or philosopher's stone by which they could multiply gold at a tremendous rate. Others hardly mention gold, but talk more in terms of cosmic opposites, and of joining the male and female — and they refer to this complete perfect thing as the 'philosopher's stone'. Others write as though their whole concern were the saving of matter, of metals and possibly of the whole world. Others, as though it is the salvation of themselves that they are about; and yet others as though they were looking for a perfect medicine, or 'elixir of life'.

But whatever their aim they all have this in common: that they are trying to find a perfect form which contains all the cosmic parts within it. They also all agree that they must first somehow reduce the metals back to a prime formless first matter. Since this matter lies *behind*, or rather *within* the metal (in both a historical and physical sense) this reduction involves going down into the secret centre of the metal, where wonderful things are found.

In contrast to this downward melting or reduction, the birth of the new metal, philosopher's stone, or young King as he is sometimes called, is seen as a purifying and fixing process. These journeys into and out of the metals correspond to the activity between the centre and circumference of the cosmos, and to the activity between material potentiality and perfect form; and they were simultaneously seen as taking place in the high or low parts of the retorts and alembics where the liquifying, distilling and fixing processes were occuring, as in a cosmic operation.

These various topics: the salvation and transmutation of metals, man's medicine, the planets, and the cosmos, are all so closely related one to another in the alchemist's mind, that he uses the terminology of them interchangeably, and will write by turns about a metal, a planet, an element, or a cosmic level, without consciously changing the subject.

Alchemists are very mysterious as to what constitutes the original matter with which to start work. They say, in fact, that here lies the great secret, and almost every alchemical experiment starts with a mystery. Some alchemists call their original matter 'lead', because this is the heaviest and darkest and dullest of the planetary metals. Others start with mercury, yet others with antimony because it resembles lead.

Later alchemists rejected the theory of the four elements, and adopted the Arabic view that everything is composed of the three principles of mercury, sulphur and salt (or spirit, soul and body). But in their work they still retained the aim of uniting all three principles in a pure form and in a perfect indissoluble cosmic harmony.

On account of this parallelism and mixing of levels alchemical terminology is very confusing, and Newton, when he was studying alchemy, tried to unravel its complexity by compiling a lexicon for himself, where he wrote down the various uses and meanings of each term as he came across them in his reading. In his entry under the word *Altitude* we can recognise the three medieval dimensions, the three principles, the spirit body and soul, and the complete cosmos, all lying together, interlocked in correspondence:

> Altitude profundity and latitude, the volatile, the fixed and the intermediary natures, spirit body and soul[...] Latitude everywhere in this globe holds an intermediary place between altitude and profundity[...] Clangor Buccinae [*the name of a book*] puts altitude for that which is manifest, profundity for that which is hidden and latitude for the intermediary between them [8].

Perhaps most revealing of all the parallelisms and correspondences in alchemical thought, is the fact that the written symbol for gold in alchemical and old chemical texts is the same as the astrological symbol for the sun, namely a circle with a dot at the centre: ⊙. And this, as we already know, is almost a diagram of the medieval created cosmos itself.

(v) *MAN*. What is the entity Man the *microcosm*, to whom this medieval cosmos is related? The term is not a mere generalisation of many men in the normal sense.

We cannot understand the medieval mind until we realise that their cosmos was a reality within which men had been living for centuries. A medieval man standing on the earth and looked up at the revolving fir-

---

[8] Keynes MS. 30, p. 5, 6.

mament of stars, knew that God was just above him, that the universe is enormous and peopled with intelligences and angels, full of light and happiness; and that the very magnitude of the world is a sign of the greatness of God. He also knew that this world had only been created a few thousand years previously, and was probably to vanish quite soon. There had been two major events since the Creation: the fall of man, and the coming of Christ. This shows that man was a unique figure: his fall was a single event, and his redemption another unique event. These great events of the universe had already happened, but they were dramatically ever-present, and the past and the future were both contained in the presence of God. Man, standing at the centre of this world, felt his sufferings and joys related to the will of God; he saw the heaven above him and felt hell below him. He was standing at the lowest yet most fruitful point of the world.

This 'uniqueness' of Man is the core of the matter. Just as there is one God and one Christ, so there is Man. When a medieval writer trained in Platonic thought and Christian theology writes about Man as *the microcosm of the world*, it does not really cross his mind that there are many thousands of men yet only one world, and the parallel is not quite right.

This medieval concept of Man only gave way to *individual men* in the 17th century. The people who look at the modern world, and study it, are individual men, in the plural. Modern observers of scientific reality are individual people, and all modern knowledge and reality is related to individuals; but the reflector of the medieval cosmos is the single Man, and medieval knowledge is related to him.

The difference between these two attitudes becomes clear when we look at medieval paintings. Their diagrammatic pictures of the cosmos are usually flat two-dimensional disks within which are contained the necessary number of concentric circles for the planets and elemental regions. It would obviously be difficult for an illuminator of manuscripts to portray a three-dimensional diagram on a piece of parchment. But this flat two-dimensional vision is in fact characteristic of medieval thought. All medieval concepts seem to have something static and two-dimensional about them. Events are mainly understood in terms of static *form* and *place*, and even motion tends to be understood very simply in two-dimensional terms: either up and down or in a circle.

Just as medieval painting is two-dimensional, so the figures of Christ and the Virgin also have a flat hieratic quality, as things that belong to a high spiritual order. They are not like solid objects in a room, united to an individual viewer in his atmospheric space. With this two-dimensional vision there is no question of imagining walking round the figure, or seeing it from different points of view; there is only a question of contemplating it or feeling its presence. The form *itself* is being portrayed, not the 'form-as-seen-from-one-individual-point-of-view'. It is not simply that medieval painters could not paint anything three-dimensional for lack of technique, it

31

is that the idea of an object to be portrayed only from one individual point of biew is a modern concept. From this, as from their idea of the microcosm, we can detect that the medieval world is concerned with universals. The elements of the world are divisions of the universal whole; Man the microcosm is a reflection of this whole; and the figures he paints are the universal figures that dominate the whole world.

These two different concepts of man — as universal and as individual — are crucial differences, as between medieval and modern thought.

(vi) *SOCIETY AS A COSMIC PATTERN.* I am concerned here mainly with cosmology, but the structure of the medieval cosmos reflects such clear correspondences into medieval society, that it is important we take note of the fact.

It was largely Christian doctrine, combined with Platonic idealism, that imposed the idea of unity or singleness in medieval society. God is the master of the world he created, and his angels are his obedient servants, ranging down in hierarchies of spirituality, from the highest archangels and angels, down to the spiritual intelligences, and finally the soul of man. Christ is a single person, all men are contained in him and in his church, and at Mass every man shares in the same spiritual redemption.

Similarly the Church itself has its unified, pyramidal structure — from the Pope, who receives direct mandate

32

and grace from God, down through the hierarchies of archbishops and bishops, to the lower orders of the church spread over the earth. Likewise, in corresponding structure, the lay feudal society has its pyramid, with the Emperor at the top receiving his direct authority from God, ranging through the feudal hierarchies, down to the lowest serf who tills the land, and is tied to the earth.

The theoretical structure of feudal society is too well known to need any detailed description; but it is important to understand its relation to the cosmos. These vertical hierarchies, from the highest to the lowest, are like the vertical spheres of the cosmos, where divine spirit and authority radiate from the highest sphere down towards the earth, and where the earth in turn raises its fruits and products up towards the higher spheres.

So the correspondence or parallels which we have seen in other branches of thought, appear also in society, relating the social status of men to the structure of the world itself.

PATTERNS OF RELATIONSHIP

Since the medieval cosmos is so different from our own 20th century reality, how are we to compare the two? We do not even have the mental concepts to understand their mind and experience except in sudden intuitive flashes. What common ground do we have with them? What common terms to relate and contrast with theirs, if we are so defective in what they experienced, and they so deficient in what we know?

Expressed in formal terms, the structure of the medieval cosmos with its internal divisions, regulates the structure of the objects within it, and determines the relation of one object to another. And this is in turn linked to Man's own place in the world. And the same pattern is repeated in society, in the relation of one man to another. In medieval thought there are therefore five interlocking relationships:

1. the *cosmos/object* relationship
2. the *object/object* relationship
3. the *man/cosmos* relationship
4. the *man/object* relationship
5. the *man/man* relationship

(1) There is a relation between the four elements and the whole world, and the philosopher's stone and the whole world. These are *object/cosmos* relationships. (2) There is the relation of one metal to another, or one element to another within the unity of the cosmos. These are *object/object* relationships. (3) There is the relation between the whole world as macrocosm, and man as microcosm reflecting it. This is the *man/cosmos* relationship. (4) There is a relation between man and the qualities of hot and cold in medicine. This is a *man/object* relationship. (5) And finally there is the structure of feudal and divine law linking one man to another within

the universality of the Microcosm, of Christ and of his Church. These are *man/man* relationships.

I believe I am right in thinking that all cosmologies contain these five relationships, though they operate differently and have different content in each cosmology.

The modern cosmos, for example, consists of matter, light and a few forces; and so do the objects within the cosmos. Therefore modern classical physics recognises a link between *relationships 1* and *2*. Modern relativity theory has shown a further link between these and *relationship 3*, by finding that our experience of the cosmos is related to our status as observers. And modern quantum mechanics has shown the relevance of *relationship 4*, where our own interference as observers determines our knowledge; not to mention the fact that the chemistry and mechanics of our bodies is the same as the chemistry and mechanics of the solar system.

Modern psychology has told us a little about *relationship 5*, as has modern Marxist theory. But on the whole *relationship 5* is a surprise. If it is found to be constantly linked with the other four relationships, then our knowledge of reality will somehow reflect our social and psychological structures, and vice versa. And if this proves to be universally applicable, it is of immense importance, and we shall have to revise our whole approach to knowledge and consciousness. One of my purposes in writing this work is to explore the importance of the fifth link.

This fifth link suggests that the type of knowledge we can gain is determined by the type of observer we have.

35

This knowledge will not only alter with the *location* of the observer, as Einstein said, it will also alter with the observer's own psychology.

Einstein has shown a cosmos relative to the observer, and has constructed *a system of the world which is true for an indefinite number of observers.*

I shall how transfer the relativism aspect over from the system to the observer himself. Taking this same relationship of observer and observed system, I shall postulate that the system alters according to the *type of observer* who is doing the observing. I shall then start to conceive of *an observer who can understand a multiple number of systems.* At present I am dealing here with only two systems, the medieval and the modern, but the foundation for multiplicity has been laid.

In order to proceed in this matter we must find out more about the observer and what is his relationship to his system. It may be possible to use the history of thought in order to trace the relationship, and so discover different types of observer. This, if anything, is what could turn the history of thought suddenly into an important subject, instead of a field for antiquarians.

For the moment I shall plod slowly on from medieval into modern thought, keeping in mind these five relationships.

36

CHAPTER II

MEDIEVAL ARTISTS DEFINE SPACE

As we have found similar patterns in various branches of medieval thought, the question arises whether one branch of thought during the Middle Ages and subsequently, was secretly leading the others. This does not appear to be so. The physicist was clearly only concerned with physics, the astronomer with astronomy, and the painter with his painting. The connection seems to be the common mentality of the people who were studying these subjects at any one time, and their common philosophical assumptions.

But if there is any priority to be sought in the changeover from the medieval to the modern mentality, it is perhaps to be found in painting. The theoretical discoveries made by medieval and modern painters run anything up to two or three hundred years ahead of corresponding changes in other fields. It is possible that European culture is essentially visual, and our reality today is what we see — as distinct from the old Jewish culture where reality was essentially what they heard.

Whatever the reason, since painting has some priority, let us deal first with painting, and watch how painters developed their work from medieval into modern times.

* * *

The ancient Greeks and Romans had almost no concept of space. Their knowledge was in terms of form, philosophy, mathematics and logic. And these topics have nothing to do with an observer nor an observed system. Therefore the ancients had almost no knowledge of physics, and no knowledge of psychology — in spite of their vast mythologies.

The practical and theoretical work done by medieval painters in defining space is therefore one of the great unacknowledged events of mankind. In their paintings they came to discover an observer in space, and defined not only his relation to the system he is observing, but the spatial relationships between the objects themselves. The modern mind almost owes its existence to this silent and amazing discovery.

What medieval painters did was to define the relationships of three-dimensional space by detaching the position of a spectator from the scene itself, thus creating an objective point of view. They also incorporated the idea of time, or a fourth dimension into their paintings, by their use of motion and light. And by the early seventeenth century all four modern dimensions had been carefully defined by painters in relationship to a self-conscious observer. This opened the way for modern physics and modern psychology. While this event was occurring a gradual shift in the *content* of the pictures also took place.

Euclid's geometry is a geometry of solid body; and the art of Greece and Rome, like their knowledge, was mainly concerned with the forms of solid bodies, as in sculpture and architecture. However, in the late Hellenistic period artists developed some subtle landscape painting, reminiscent of modern impressionists both in mood and in outdoor lighting. In some Roman paintings, as at Pompeii, the small figures are placed in a landscape with a clear horizon line, and the figures cast shadows, and are correctly proportioned to each other on the receding ground. But there is nothing to show that the Romans knew anything about a vanishing point, nor that painters had any theoretical knowledge of perspective. In architecture they were approaching an understanding of perspective drawing, but the principles were never fully worked out [9].

Early Christian painters began the task all over again. Curiously enough they first telescoped this three-dimensional atmospheric vision of the Romans back into flat, two-dimensional shapes. This was an important first step — though it has often been mistaken for a retrograde one. First they flattened the land and sky so that these become merely horizontal bars of colour running across the painting, and look like strips ranging up the surface of the picture in hierarchical strata. The shadows cast by the figures are made to stand up straight, and are then eliminated, so that the figures themselves

---

[9] For reproductions of some of the works discussed here, see M. S. Bunim: *Space in medieval painting, and the forerunners of perspective.* New York, 1940.

no longer stand on a horizontal earth, but are placed on the actual surface of the picture, hieratically. The themes are now mainly religious. Often the background to the pictures is painted blue or gold, and the figures themselves seem to shine from a divine area. We are in a world where man is an insignificant and almost powerless being, faced by the tremendous and immediate spiritual presence of God, of Christ, and of the angels. And the paintings are flat. Instead of man looking into the picture, the divine figures in the picture are looking at man. This general change occurs in early Christian mosaics, such as those at Ravenna, and in some early paintings.

Technically speaking the four open dimensions of late Roman painting have thus been crushed and collapsed back into two. (I shall refer to light as indicating a fourth dimension). The third and fourth dimensions have not been discarded as they might be in the pattern of a table-cloth, they have been telescoped and are being held in *reserve*. Since the objects portrayed are now universal, much greater in power than the man who has painted them, this technique is quite correct. The painted figures are no longer limited to any particular place, they are not imprisoned in a room, they are eternal. Christ stands or sits like a giant, often encircled by an almond-shaped halo or mandorla which marks him off and raises him above the world of mankind; while at his feet the minute figures of men are seen, subject to his will and judgment.

So in early Christian art we have a helpless Man faced with great powers, and the painted figures are restricted or delimited by only *two* defined dimensions.

The illuminated manuscripts leading through the Carolingian period introduce the next change. The flat surfaces against which the figures are standing begin to be adorned by geometrical patterns. Sometimes a smaller rectangle is drawn inside the picture, so that it seems to be doubly framed. At other times there are rough repeated circles or simple shapes covering the background in a regular design. By this means the background surface is measured or squared off, and provides something like a geometrical grid system against which the figures stand. It is the beginning of measured, controlled space. This habit of covering the background with designs increased steadily throughout the Middle Ages.

Romanesque architecture shows a development similar to that of painting. Greek and Roman buildings had been made of classical *forms:* the column, the portico, the triangular pediment. But Romanesque shows a new interest in empty, heavy *surfaces.* Both inside and outside a Romanesque church, with its ponderous solid columns and body, there are large empty areas, that do not have the shape of any classical form, and on which are placed small geometrical designs or even whole tiers of arches. It is as though a spiritual presence is breathing through these vast solid surfaces.

Perhaps some conclusion can be drawn from this

change. Greek life is associated with sculptured form, the Jewish spirit is free of all representation, and the Christian from an early age has been associated with surface, and then with space. Perhaps the Christian idea of soul helped man to separate himself from matter and solid body, to a degree that was difficult for the Greeks, and this made possible modern scientific detachment and the separation of the observer from the physical world. Since scientific 'objectivity' was largely worked out in terms of space, there may be some connection between the Christian idea of soul or spirit, surface in art, the discovery of space, and the scientific method.

The next change in definition of space comes with Gothic. From the twelfth century onwards the solid architecture of the Romanesque gives way to a lighter style constructed on the principle of crossed arches, and the aspiring arch. Romanesque is a style grounded on internal *body*. Gothic is an architecture of internal *space*. It defines and directs the space inside the church. The external façade draws the viewer into the church, and the Gothic arch leads the eye and the mind not only along the nave, but more urgently up towards the heavens. It is an open and expanding system of perspective. Gothic is the first style in European architecture where space rather than body is being represented [10].

---

[10] The great mistake the Victorians made in the Gothic revival was not to notice that Gothic is an *internal* architecture; they plastered the exterior surfaces of buildings with Gothic shapes, and thought they had achieved the Gothic manner.

42

What is this Gothic space? Gothic aspiration has been misleadingly called spiritual. In fact it shows a new spatial *separation* between man and God. We now have a world of man down below on earth, and separate from it a spiritual world of God up in the heavens, and Gothic architecture is the path that leads the eye up from one to the other. It is an open system of perspective, a readiness to receive God's presence, and a human aspiration towards heaven. Where the Bible says *'in* earth as it is *in* heaven', it signified two different states of existence. But these two states have now become two *places,* and the journey from one to the other has become a change of place: it is *on* the earth, and up *in* the heavens.

Gothic architecture has direction. God, who had previously been an absolute and universal figure — much more universal than man — is now seen specifically from man's point of view, and though Man had previously been only a fragment of God's world, God now only belongs at one end of a human aspiration, and is slowly drifting further and further away as the human world of space expands. Space is therefore being used to describe the separation between man and God; and the space marks out a new area of human experience.

This Gothic change shows a new activity on Man's side. He is no longer the silent sufferer of spiritual forces. A new religious movement started up in the twelfth century, based on an imitation of Christ. Theologians began to view God in more abstract terms, and Christ and the Virgin in a more human way. There was an attempt

43

on the part of many people to follow in Christ's steps and re-live or imitate his experiences. This produced groups of heretics, such as the Waldenses and the Cathari, and led to clashes with the church. But the same movement surfaced inside the Church itself with St. Francis of Assisi, perhaps the most distinguished of the group, who received the stigmata of the cross on his own body.

This whole movement shows a novel type of human self-reliance; the world is becoming more and more the scene of man's behaviour. This new importance of human things vis a vis the universe appears also in the *content* of Gothic art. The sculptures of Chartres are more gentle, even the divine figures seem to have human proportions and feelings. The feminine attractive quality of the Virgin is more marked. By the time we reach the 14th and 15th centuries Christ is being depicted with entirely human proportions and human emotions, far removed from the terrifying apocalyptic judge of earlier centuries.

Technically therefore, the Gothic alignment of aspiration and open perspective shows a primitive description of three-dimensional space, and a corresponding drop in the universality and magnitude of the figures represented. It also shows man starting to define his place between the cosmic opposites. Greek philosophers had explained the world's activity as an interaction between universal opposites: fire and water, the One and the Many, and so on. During the early Middle Ages these opposites were increasingly visualised as *vertical* opposites, ranging

44

between the circumference and centre of the world, with heaven above and hell below. In Gothic architecture the alignment is carried one stage further, and man's status in the middle, with heaven above and hell below him — what I have called *pattern 2* — is clearly defined. The final step was taken in the sixteenth century, when man moved back out of the picture altogether to view the cosmic opposites of up and down, or hot and cold, as merely a continuous scale of dimension and temperature, with no opposition left to them.

Early Gothic illuminated manuscripts and paintings also reveal these first stages of a controlled three-dimensional space. The background surfaces are now more intricately worked. The large geometrical patterns that had covered Romanesque paintings like a rough grid system, become smaller and more delicate, and often include leaves and flowers, and other natural objects; the surface before which the figures stand is frequently filled in completely, as in a tapestry. And the figures themselves, which had previously shone from a spiritual world of blue or gold, are now brought slightly forward and made to stand on little foot-rests. They are no longer the old divine and enigmatic figures commanding the world and facing it. Their power and stature seems to be limited by the gay patterned area behind them. And since they are now placed a little forward there is the first suggestion of a space in depth, and of a spectator looking through the frame into the picture.

Early Gothic architecture was perhaps mainly concerned with open vertical space, but early Gothic painting shows the first suggestion of horizontal space in depth.

The next change was the transformation or lowering of this Gothic vertical space into the complete horizontal space of the Renaissance. This was achieved as man stepped gradually back and out of his field of vision altogether, to view everything along the horizontal line of the earth. At this point the observer will become detached from the things he is observing.

The change from Gothic to Renaissance was complicated. In northern Europe it took the form of a series of disintegrations. The simple pointed arch was broken down to the little spikes or focuses of the flamboyant style, and fragmented into many angular directions; as though the unified medieval vision were breaking up. The feeling of aspiration is lost, and the intricacy of the patterns and stonework become of interest in themselves. A similar fragmentation was taking place in late medieval philosophy. The other stylistic change, misleadingly named 'perpendicular Gothic', is a more direct step into the Renaissance. In this the internal space is brought under the control of regular vertical lines, which eliminate almost all traces of vertical subdivisions. The effect is a box-like, almost unified space, with practically no aspiration, and with the basic proportions of firm horizontal vision.

But the most important contribution of northern Europe at this point was perhaps the careful study of light, applied with the new oil techniques by the Van Eyck brothers and other Flemish painters. They began to use light as a unifying element, so that all the objects painted are held in one atmospheric medium, and fixed in one specific place. The subject matter of painting was likewise shifting: there is a much greater interest in individual portraits, and a new interest in individual psychology — an interest which was to reach fruition in the first plays of the Renaissance.

In southern Europe, where Gothic architecture was never of any great importance, the main achievement of the later Middle Ages was the development of a full three-dimensional perspective space. The tentative spaces in Gothic painting were developed here. The background was extended in greater depth to form a room, or interior, with tiled floors and patterned surfaces creating the first rudiments of three-dimensional perspective vision. The figures are now standing in a room as in a box. But in these 14th century paintings of Giotto, Duccio and the Lorenzetti brothers, the receding lines of the floor and walls only tend towards a small vanishing *area,* they do not yet come to one focal point. This more than anything else indicates that perspective vision was seen roughly by the eye, and understood by the mind, before it was calculated theoretically.

With these Siennese and Florentine paintings, where the figures are now contained inside a room or area, the spectator is looking directly through the picture frame, as through a window, and into the picture along the lines of the buildings. The space in which the spectator himself is standing seems to be projected right into the picture, and the picture has therefore become an extension of the spectator's world, not as in earlier paintings, part of a separate divine presence.

In the fifteenth century, Brunelleschi painted an architectural scene to be viewed by the spectator from one *exact* prescribed place and distance from the picture. Viewed from this precise spot the painted scene appeared entirely realistic. This was full theoretical perspective painting. And here comes the surprise: The geometrical control which had been achieved by Gothic painters on a flat board has therefore suddenly been projected backwards and out into the real space in which the spectator is standing. The spectator himself is now standing in a space that is controlled by the carefully measured areas of the picture. Perspective space gives detachment, but it also captures and controls the spectator's own position in real space.

This final theoretical discovery of perspective in the Renaissance was only the climax of what had been achieved slowly over many centuries, and shows how far the medieval world of internal forms was being replaced by a new controlled space relating the observer and the objects one to another, externally. The 15th century architect Alberti was one of the first to formulate the theory of perspective painting:

> First then upon the surface whereon I am working, I
> draw a square composed of right angles, as large as

I think convenient; and this serves me as a window through which I am to view the story which is to be painted. Then I determine how large I will draw a man, and divide his height into three parts[...] With this measure I then divide the lower line of the square which I have drawn, into as many such parts as it will admit; and this lower line of the square is with me proportional to the next parallel transverse quantity seen on the fictitious pavement.

Then I make one single point where the sight is to be directed within the square, which point is in the exact place where the central ray of vision is to strike, for which reason I call it the central point (or vanishing point). It has a very proper effect to set this point not higher from the ground line than we intend to make the height of the man that we are to draw: because by this means the beholder and the objects painted will seem to be upon the same plane.

Having fixed this central point I must draw straight lines from that to each of the divisions of the lower straight line of the square; which line informs me in what manner I must contract the transverse quantities to the view, in order to proceed to the most remote and almost infinite distance [11].

Alberti insists that 'no painted object can appear like the real, unless its distance from the beholder's eye be fixed by some certain rule'. He is quite specific that painting is only concerned with surfaces, and the external motion of bodies in space. The painter,

---

[11] From *The Paintings of Leon Battista Alberti in three books. Translated by James Leoni.* London 1726, p. 8.

is to desire nothing so much as that on that single surface [of a painting...] the forms of a number of surfaces may be truly represented (p. 6).
Motions are either of the mind, which the learned call affections or passions, such as anger, grief, fear, joy, desire and the like; or else of the body[...] We painters must only consider that motion which is said to be made when the body changes its situation (p. 19).

His only reason for using man's body as the unit of measurement is that it is our normal gage of relative size:

Man is of all things best known to Man [...and therefore] whatever sort of bodies we draw in a picture, will appear large or small according to the size of Men that are drawn in the same piece (p. 7b).

Like the Van Eyck brothers, he feels that light is more important than colour because

the accession of light and shade shows in what part the Superficies rises, and where it sinks, and how much each part declines or bends; so the right placing his white and black is what must obtain him the praise[...] that his works should have a bold relief (p. 20).

Like almost all the other artists of the 15th century, Alberti links painting with the new interest in mechanics.

I have observed in Man that in all his attitudes he brings his whole body under his head, as being the most weighty of all the members. Thus if he rests his whole body upon one foot, that foot, like the base of a column, is always perpendicular under his head (p. 19).

Leonardo da Vinci took the same view of painting. Leonardo writes:

> Painting extends only to the surface of bodies[...] painting is philosophy, because philosophy deals with the increase and decrease through motion[...] Painting can be shown to be philosophy because it deals with the motion of bodies in the promptitude of their actions [12].

The remarkable thing is that all this theoretical work on space, detaching the observer, relating him spatially to observed objects, and fixing his position, was achieved by the sixteenth century without the use of the word *space*. The modern concept of *space* did not come into full being until about a hundred years later.

By the time of the Renaissance, painters had defined this new system of external or spatial relationships. But man was still living inside the medieval world, the world was still composed of static forms, and objects still had their own secret and internal qualities or personalities. Even in painting the medieval and classical forms have not been eliminated. Painting has only expressed or defined three dimensions — the fourth dimension of time

_____

[12] *Literary Sources of Art History*, p. 171.

was not exposed until the Baroque — and in the Renaissance the painted figures still have a universality and timeless quality about them. Renaissance architecture, which is less spectacular than painting, shows up this fact: it is a static façade-type architecture composed of classical shapes, with circles, squares or triangles placed on its surfaces. Yet notice that Renaissance architecture, as a *façade* architecture, was therefore an architecture seen essentially from the *outside*. And the only relationships that are being avidly explored are the new external relationships of space, which are slowly breaking down the old world and linking everything in a new way.

European architecture was therefore progressing from body to space, from an internal view of body to an external view of space, in the following way: Romanesque is an internal view of body, Gothic is an internal view of space; classical Renaissance is an external view of body, and Baroque will finally be an external view of movement in space.

*　*　*

We have been following here a great shift in the *man/ object* relationship. Man has stepped gradually back and now views everything along the horizontal lines of space. This shift has brought a corresponding change in the *object/object* relationships. All objects are now related to each other through space. A greater and more self-conscious control of the *man/object* relationship has produced

52

a new relation between one object and the next, and vice versa.

When the painted divine figures were universal, painting was two-dimensional. As the figures become smaller and less powerful we get three-dimensional painting. This indicates that the added *definition* of objects in space is reducing their stature, and the third dimension imprisons the objects or figures more and more, and lowers their universality; or else it confirms that their universality has already been lowered.

During this gradual detachment and increased control, man himself has become more human. There is a growing interest in portraiture, in individual psychology and in character. Man has by now grown so much greater in stature in relation to his world, that instead of reflecting the cosmos in himself, it is now felt by the Renaissance that the cosmos reflects him, and that 'man is the measure of all things'. So there has also been a silent and corresponding change in the *man/cosmos* relationship. Previously the great cosmic qualities of the elements had been thought to cause melancholy and gaiety in him; but with the gradual detachment of the observer from the physical world these cosmic qualities decline, and melancholy and gaiety appear as human attributes. A distinct separation is now beginning to occur between those qualities that will be termed 'subjective' or human, and those that will be thought of as 'objective' or physically in space.

Therefore the general transition of medieval to Renais-

53

sance art shows us that the observer gradually stepped *back,* and put a distance between himself and the objects he was viewing, expressed in terms of a new controlled space. But in another respect it is the individual man who took the initiative, and instead of suffering the powers of the spiritual world, drove *forward* through the frame of the picture, right to the horizon, chasing the spiritual world away and capturing the whole area for himself by means of space.

This self-conscious awareness of the observer's position in painting and art — viewing everything in terms of space — is the development that astronomy and almost every other branch of thought was to follow during the 16th and 17th centuries.

*   *   *

I must formulate clearly what we have so far discovered: By the end of the Renaissance man had stepped back and created for the first time in history a controlled space related to himself, in which all objects are contained and measured. Determining the position of an observer is merely a technical matter, useful for perspective but of no other particular application. Historically, however, it was so intimately bound up with the appreciation of space as a medium of relationships, that it clearly had deep significance. It provides a clue to the fact that historically speaking space is not so much a physical fact as a *method of thinking*. It was by detaching and defining

54

this position of the individual observer relative to the picture, that the new system of relationships was achieved, and space as we know it today was formulated. Modern space could almost be described as the relation of the *individual* viewer to the objects around him. Only one man can be at any one point in space at any one time. The medieval idea of universal Man had disappeared. And as this new pattern of relationships emerged, the content of the pictures themselves gradually changed.

Therefore we have established two important facts:

1. Whereas the medieval world is related to a universal Man, who is standing nowhere in particular, the modern scientific world of space is related to the individual.
2. By *defining* his status as observer, man alters the type of relationships he observes, and hence the content of the observed world itself.

CHAPTER III

MECHANICS SHIFT OVER FROM INTERNAL FORM TO MOVEMENT IN SPACE

It must be apparent by now that in describing how man stepped outside his own field of vision to see the world in spatial terms, I could have explained the same phenomenon by saying that man slowly distinguished his own human qualities and emotions from the physical world, and gradually withdrew them. This is the more traditional way of describing the historical events preceding the Cartesian dualism. However, this commonly accepted explanation makes the mistake of regarding space as an absolute external reality, and other qualities as imaginary or internal to man. That is why I have avoided it. I have tried to show, on the contrary, that space is as much a mental construct and a part of man's mentality as anything else. At any one historical period men call some things *objective* (or external to themselves) and other things *subjective* (or internal to themselves). That they should do so is historically important. But it is incorrect to state that any things, either objective or subjective, are absolutely so independent of human thought. The demarcation line is constantly shifting and creates altering patterns.

I have therefore described this particular historical

event in terms of *internal* and *external*, rather than subjective and objective, not because this is any better terminology in itself, but because it describes the relationship as it appeared when the change-over from medieval to modern thought took place. In the fifteenth, sixteenth and seventeenth centuries we witness two contrasting systems of thought lying side by side: the medieval world of form and cosmic qualities lying *inside* objects, and the modern world of space lying *outside* objects, and relating one object to another externally by means of space. Curiously enough this is how the observers also felt that they themselves were related to their knowledge: the medieval thinker declaring that he stood at the centre of the world, the modern thinker declaring that he was viewing it from a detached position. During three centuries, from the 15th to the 17th centuries, both worlds were to exist side by side as internal and external systems.

The struggle between the two worlds was ultimately a struggle between two different methods of analysis: The modern method is by encroaching on a unit or body, breaking it down to its component parts, and bringing the relationship of the parts into the world of space; the medieval method on the other hand is by analysing an undifferentiated unit into its opposite qualities without destroying the original whole. Modern thought is therefore an accumulated external relationship of parts, medieval thought is the internal division of unity. Modern thought can divide indefinitely into smaller and smaller fractions, medieval reality ultimately stops at irreducible forms.

When I say that modern thought analyses from the *outside* inwards I do not mean this only in a spatial sense: it analyses anything down to its parts, and the relationship between its parts is then *external*, not contained in any unity other than the relationships themselves. All relationships in modern knowledge are in this sense external relationships.

Since modern thought during the 16th and 17th centuries advanced by analysing bodies down to their parts, it is natural that the medieval world should remain hiding in the unit that had not yet been analysed. So medieval cosmology was chased down by external analysis to smaller and smaller internal qualities within the body. For about a hundred years the two systems were more or less equally balanced. But by the time that Descartes announced the final separation of the observer from his system, there were hardly any qualities left in objects, other than that of space or extension. In one field alone, chemistry, where it was still found impossible to analyse chemical bodies down to their atomic parts, medieval cosmology survived right into the eighteenth century, hidden inside chemical bodies.

The really significant fact is not that I am using any particular terminology here, nor even that any particular method of analysis was in progress, but that there is a curious permanent link between these two events: when *objects* are thought to have internal qualities *(model A)*,

59

man is said to be inside his world *(model B);* whereas when *objects* are said to be related externally in space *(model A)* the *observer* is said to stand apart and detached *(model B)*. What is this repeated link between *model A* and *model B?* What does it reveal about human knowledge? Obviously something profound.

Jung has tried to explain the phenomenon with his psychological theory of 'projection'. But his theory evades the issue, and is philosophically incorrect: it pre-assumes that there is one absolute objective/subjective demarcation line, and that all deviations from it are 'projections' or psychological misunderstandings.

The fact that there is a constant *shifting* between what is regarded as objective and subjective, is almost more important than a definition of the terms themselves.

* * *

The struggle between two systems of thought during the fifteenth, sixteenth and seventeenth centuries occurred over a few vital issues. I have described the modern move of the painter to detach himself from the picture by the new method of perspective. Art has shown us that a greater self-consciousness (a change in the *man/object* relationship) reduced the numinous content of the pictures (a change in *object/object* relationships).

We shall now follow the reverse effect in mechanics, where a new study of moving objects automatically coincides with a shift in man's objectivity. The terminology of mechanics is different from the language of painting, but the major changes are the same. Scientists managed to discard gradually a medieval mechanics of irreducible static forms, and came to understand the trajectory of bodies moving freely in space.

Medieval thinkers, like the Greeks before them, tended to make a distinction between form or order which can be understood, and chaos or formlessness and confusion which cannot. It is difficult for us today to understand the difference, because we would argue that everything that has shape has form — we cannot conceive of 'degrees' of creation, formlessness, or differentiation. But for them *form* was an ideal that belonged to an intellectual order of things, whereas dark matter did not. And *form* or *ideal* did not mean to them what they mean to us now. They meant something that can be conceived as an idea, that has intellectual order — as distinct from other aspects of nature which have no revealed order.

This duality between the comprehensible and the incomprehensible, between the differentiated and the undifferentiated, is what underlies the medieval distinction between form and chaos. Any attempt to understand anything therefore was always in terms of form.

The Middle Ages inherited two theories of form from the Greeks: that of Plato's *Timaeus*, and that of Aristotle. The Aristotelian theory which is essentially biological was generally applied to terrestrial things, and the Platonic one which is mathematical, was mainly applied to heavenly bodies.

The Aristotelian theory is that each body has an appetite or wish to fulfill its *essence*. A pear seed, for example, is in *essence* a full-grown tree, and it will grow into a pear tree, which it potentially is, by its own wish or motive power. The motive power lies within the seed itself.

In mechanics the Aristotelian theory is that any motion is either *inherent* in the body itself, as part of the body's essence, and is therefore *natural* motion; or else is exerted from the outside, as when one body pushes another, which is *violent* motion. Natural motion, being inherent in the body, is by far the more important; violent motion is only accidental and temporary. In the world at large the heavens move *naturally* in a circle, and elemental objects move *naturally* up and down in straight lines by levity or gravity.

This animistic view of motion originates from the fact that Aristotle was a biologist, and living beings can feel the difference between acting and being pushed. Such a theory of motive power is ultimately static. It explains motion as the property of a form, and relies on the medieval system of cosmic opposites for its motivation and dynamism. Internal and external are *opposites*, natural and violent motion are *opposites*, action and passion are *opposites*, gravity and levity are *opposites*, and natural motion occurs between these opposites. Like the whole medieval anthropomorphic system, this pattern of opposites gradually faded away as man withdrew himself from events, and all motion was reduced to one level — motion in space.

According to Aristotelian physics even motion and stillness are two opposite qualities. The law of inertia was thought to apply only to bodies that are still. Bodies need no other cause for remaining still; but to be in constant motion they must have a constant cause. A body must be continuously pushed, or it must have a constant motive appetite within itself.

The Aristotelian theory was well equipped to explain falling bodies: they have an appetite to fall naturally downwards. Aristotelians explained the acceleration of a falling body by saying that the body moves more jubilantly every moment as it finds itself nearer home; but they sometimes allowed that a diminishing column of air below the body might be causing a diminishing resistance.

The difficulty came in trying to explain the motion of a projectile, because a projectile is hurled. This is violent motion, and once it has left the hands of the thrower a projectile appears to have no constant cause pushing it on. There could be no motive cause in the object itself, since the motion is violent. Some Aristotelians believed that the continued motion of the projectile might be due to the air in front rushing to the back to prevent a vacuum; they even thought that the projectile might accelerate by this means. They could not of course visualise projectile motion in a vacuum because they had no conception of empty space.

However, in Paris in the fourteenth century, Jean Buridan and Nicholas Oresme propounded a novel theory of *impetus:* that a projectile is in fact carried forward in its course by an impetus that it acquires from the mere fact of being in motion. This impetus was sometimes described as a thing inside the body, and sometimes as an impetuosity which has been imparted to it by the thrower, rather as heat is imparted to a metal rod. This theory was therefore veering away from the idea of innate motion towards the idea of imparted motion. Once the impetuosity was exhausted it was believed that the *natural* motion of the body took over, and the body fell down to earth in a straight line. The course of a projectile was therefore seen as a *violent* or imparted motion in a straight line, followed by a *natural* straight line motion downwards. It was even realised that these two forces might work together. As one type of motion was taking over from the other, the projectile might move in a circle, rather like a string passing over a wheel and falling to the ground.

The advantage of this new theory of impetus over the Aristotelian theory is that it can be understood as occurring in a vacuum, whereas Aristotelian *violent* motion could not. And in the fourteenth century the universities of Oxford and Paris began to explore the idea of vacuum as a physical possibility.

However, the actual path which the projectile takes was still described in terms of static classical forms. The circle and the straight line were, to the medieval mind, the only natural forms of motion.

This treatment of motion in terms of static form was

also prevalent in astronomy. It had been realised very early on that the planets do not run the simple circular course that Aristotle had described. Their complicated progressions, retrogressions and visible variations of speed, had been plotted more exactly by Ptolemy in terms of small additional revolutions called epicycles, made by each planet within the body of its own sphere. Throughout the Middle Ages any additional irregularities and variations observed in planetary motion were explained by adding a few more of these epicycles or small circular revolutions, like interlocking wheels or spokes; and by the end of the Middle Ages the motion of the planets was described in terms of a very complicated series of circular motions of varying degrees of size, rather like the wheels of a watch. But it did not apparently occur to anyone to question that heavenly motion, being pure and constant, could be anything but circular. The concept of the *circle* and the *straight line* as pure forms dominated all studies of planetary and terrestrial motion.

* * *

The next advance in the study of projectile motion was greatly helped both by the revival of Platonism, and by the study of projective geometry.

During the early Renaissance there was a new interest in Plato's mathematical theory of form. The Platonic view of form as geometry and number, which had mainly been applied to astronomy, was now extended to terrestrial things and to terrestrial movement — thus linking heavenly and terrestrial physics in terms of mathematics. The more mathematical concepts of Plato gradually replaced the Aristotelian theory of essence which, with its heavy addendum of potentiality and chaos, had so far dominated terrestrial physics. It became possible to study movement on earth in terms simply of number and geometry, without any internal Aristotelian qualities of body.

The pure geometry of the heavens began to descend to earth, but it changed its heavenly quality as it did so. As Platonic forms were increasingly applied to particular terrestrial activities, there was a corresponding loss in their *ideal* and *universal* aspect. (This deserves a note: One of the greatest mistakes medieval historians have made is to treat 'Platonism' or 'Aristotelianism' as definite bodies of thought which reappear at irregular intervals during the Middle Ages. The Platonism of one century was in fact quite different from the Platonism of another, and it is more correct to study each age's thought in its own framework, and within its own pattern of relationships, than to assess it in terms of Plato or Aristotle, however much these authors were being read. A reader interprets and incorporates what he reads into his own mentality).

In the first half of the sixteenth century the study of projectile motion was taken up as a ballistic problem by Niccolo Tartaglia for the purpose of tracking the path of a cannon ball or bullet. He calculated in 1537 that the

66

trajectory was composed of two forces working together: the force or impetus from the initial throw, and the downward force of gravity. This produced a path consisting of two straight lines, with the arc of a circle where one force took over from the other. However, in 1546 Tartaglia stated that the force of gravity is effective from the first moment that the ball leaves the cannon, and therefore the trajectory never in fact moves along a straight line. Leonardo da Vinci, some years previously, had drawn the path of a projectile as a constant curve [13].

A new influence on mechanics came with the discovery of projective geometry. This greatly modified, and finally dispersed, the Platonic conception of absolute irreducible geometric forms. Painters of perspective had already discovered that a circle is only a circle when seen from a certain point of view; viewed from an angle it appears to be an ellipse. Dürer demonstrated, for example, that if you project a circle onto a plane at an angle to the original one, the circle becomes an ellipse. Projective geometry and the new study of optics were related to this work on perspective. It was found that all geometric forms differ according to the angle from which they are observed. But principally it was discovered that if you intersect the circular cone of vision from different angles, it yields a variety of curves: a

---

[13] For further information see A. R. Hall: *Ballistics in the Seventeenth Century*, 1952.

circle, an ellipse, a parabola, a hyperbola, and ultimately two intersecting straight lines. Between a circle and straight lines there were therefore appearing in nature a number of alternative curves. The first result of this work on conic sections was that the ellipse, the parabola and the hyperbola joined the circle as intelligible forms. But the study was still proceeding in terms of static form or shapes.

In 1590 an English astronomer Thomas Digges was discussing 'whether the upper part of the circuit made with the bullet be a portion of a circle as Tartaglia supposeth' or 'whether it be not rather a Conical Section, and different at every several randon. (Nearer but not perfect conical, but rather helical),' or 'Whether it be not at the utmost randon a section parabolical in all kind of pieces, and to differ in greatness according to the cone that to every several cylinder or piece of ordinance is convenient' [14]. Digges thought that a theory for the motion of a projectile could be calculated, rather like the theory of planetary motion.

A similar development in pure geometric form took place in astronomy. Medieval astronomers had imagined all planetary motion as circular; the heavens being perfect and the circle being the only perfect form. But projective geometry had now expanded the number of known curved forms. When Kepler, with his wide knowledge of optics, calculated in the early seventeenth

[14] Thomas Digges: *Stratioticos,* p. 356.

century that Mars moves round the sun in an *elliptical* course, he felt that he had discovered a new Platonic harmony in the heavens, and had demonstrated that the solar system has perfect proportion.

However, these discoveries and expansions of Platonic form gradually tended to break down the concept of absolute form altogether. Conic sections were followed by the discovery of a wider number of mechanical curves which could only be plotted algebraically. This disintegration of form was hastened by a radical change in the concept of number, and by the invention of more complex mathematics.

It is important to realise that in the medieval theory of numbers as internal divisions of unity, the zero does not exist and has no place. But during the later Middle Ages there came into common use a symbol for zero, which was first drawn as a comma or point, and then a small circle. In the fifteenth century the plus and minus signs also started to appear in connection with merchandise. At first these were only used as credit and debit signs, signifying *add* one or *subtract* one. But by mid-sexteenth century the English mathematician Robert Recorde was using these signs as attributes of the numbers themselves. He treated a minus number as a number in its own right. The zero had replaced man at the centre. Numbers came gradually to be viewed as a long line stretching away infinitely in both directions like a spatial coordinate, passing through zero and one, and devoid of any centre or place. Number was no longer an internal division of unity.

By the seventeenth century mathematics had advanced astonishingly. Galileo and Descartes invented an algebraic geometry with a free system of coordinates, where it is possible to plot on a graph the path of a moving body without recourse to any idea of absolute form or place, or to any static recognisable shapes. The transfer from static form to dynamic motion in space was progressing rapidly.

The next stage in the study of projectile motion made use of this new mathematics. The first attempt to plot the course of a projectile mathematically was made by Diego Uffano, who published his work in 1613. But the greatest theoretical step was taken by Galileo who, as the virtual inventor of modern dynamics, was particularly concerned to solve the problem of projectile motion. In 1632 he published work showing that a projectile always falls the same height in the same time, whether it is thrown up in the air or horizontally. But he made a mistake in his deductions and did not properly plot the curve of motion. It was Cavalieri who showed later in the same year — using Galileo's law of falling bodies — that a projectile moves in a parabolic curve. Cavalieri plotted the curve between rectangular coordinates, marking off the horizontal and vertical distances traversed, and thus proving that the curve of a trajectory is parabolic. Galileo later completed his own work, and showed that a projectile will move in a parabolic curve in

70

empty or abstract space, free of any other interfering or resisting medium. Galileo (who significantly enough was interested in Platonic thought) was satisfied that he had solved the problem at a perfect theoretical level and had demonstrated the presence of a pure conic section in natural motion. However, it was slowly realised that the air resistance on a projectile is so great, that the curve of the trajectory is in fact much more complicated, and does not conform to any conic section.

The work on motion in resisting mediums was the next problem tackled, and this was found to need a more high-powered mathematics. The curve that Newton reached for a body moving in a resisting medium was nearer to a hyperbola, but he was unable to solve the problem. Huyghens similarly calculated that the resistance varies with the square of the velocity of a projectile, but he was also unable, with his traditional mathematical knowledge, to plot the curve of motion. It was only in the early eighteenth century that Johann Bernoulli, using Leibnitz' differential calculus, managed to formulate the fundamental differential equation of ballistics.

So the study of projectile motion ran its full course from medieval into modern thought, shifting over from static internal form to dynamic motion in space. Setting out with only the Aristotelian and Platonic concepts of the circle and the straight line as *forms* of motion, it had developed geometry to accept the ellipse, the parabola and the hyperbola as intelligible forms. Even the circle, of all medieval forms the most 'internal' (the world was said to be spherical because the sphere contains the maximum volume of any shape) — even the circle had passed through perspective and projective geometry to become only one among a number of curves. The concept of motion in terms of form was finally discarded altogether, and with the instrument of algebraic geometry and differential calculus all motion was seen as motion in space, and was plotted accordingly at every instant of time. Any traces of Platonic form had disappeared and motion was now understood in spatial terms.

At the very time that the ideal forms of Platonism were analysed out of existence, the corresponding Aristotelian concept of *essence* and internal quality in bodies (together with the whole system of cosmic opposites) was similarly discarded.

The traditional medieval view had been that a body has the cause of *natural* motion within it, as an internal property. With the theory of impetus, the work on vacuum, and the plotting of projectile motion, the law of inertia was gradually revised: the distinction between natural and violent motion was discarded, stillness and motion were no longer treated as necessary opposites. With the disappearance of internal motivation and the decline of cosmic opposites came the new law of inertia, applicable to all bodies in space whether they are moving or still. But this elimination of cosmic opposites — of hot and cold, and of up and down — is, as we have seen, an expression of man's withdrawal from the centre of things to become a detached observer.

The new law of inertia was defined by Occam, Galileo, Hobbes and Descartes before it took its final shape in Newton's laws of motion. But interestingly enough it was Hobbes who pointed out this link between the withdrawal of the observer from physical events, the elimination of inner and outer qualities in bodies, and the new law of inertia. Hobbes opens chapter 2 of the *Leviathan* by stating the old law of inertia:

> That when a thing lies still, unless somewhat else stir it, it will lie still for ever, is a truth that no man doubts of.

He then proposes its extension to cover bodies in motion:

> But that when a thing is in motion, it will eternally be in motion, unless something else stay it, though the reason be the same, (namely that nothing can change it self), is not so easily assented to.

The reason for not assenting to it, he says, is that in the past we have imposed our own feelings onto inanimate things:

> For men measure, not only other men, but all other things, by themselves: and because they find themselves subject after motion to pain, and lassitude, think everything else grows weary of motion, and seeks repose of its own accord;

73

This unintentional confusion, he points out, is at the heart of the medieval schoolmen's thought:

> From hence it is, that the Schools say, Heavy bodies fall downwards, out of an appetite to rest, and to conserve their nature in that place which is most proper for them; ascribing appetite and Knowledge of what is good for their conservation, (which is more than man has) to things inanimate, absurdly.

And so, withdrawing these human feelings from inanimate things, he propounds the new law of inertia:

> When a Body is once in motion, it moveth (unless something else hinder it) eternally; and whatsoever hindreth it, cannot in an instant, but in time, and by degrees quite extinguish it.

This law of inertia was important because it withdrew human desire as the motive force in nature, and substituted in its place a new kind of physical motion and mechanical activity. This new law of inertia treats *rest* (which is place itself) and *motion* in space as the same in kind. Therefore place has disappeared.

This development of projectile mechanics during the later Middle Ages and into the 17th century, shifting from form to motion, and from internal qualities to external relationships, reveals a change in the *object/ object* relationship: a change from an internal to an external system. And the new law of inertia shows how this change interlocks with a corresponding shift in the *man/object* and *man/cosmos* relationships.

74

CHAPTER IV

NOMINALISM DESTROYS REALISM.
A THEORY OF KNOWLEDGE

Having followed changes that were taking place during
the later Middle Ages in the relationship between man,
objects and cosmos, we must now turn to the fifth relationship of *man with man*. But here we come up against
a blank. What is this thing called 'man'?

We know that man is the *subject* of his own knowledge.
So let us assume for the moment that knowledge consists
of a *subject* (thinker) and an *object* (his thought) — though
we shall have occasion to question even this assumption
later on. The relationships we have so far been observing are therefore *object/object* and *object/subject* relationships; whereas the *man/man* relationship is a *sub-
ject/subject* relationship. But what is a *subject?*

A great deal is known about *objects* but apparently nothing is known about *subjects* — no work has ever been
done on them. They defy efforts to study them. All
attempts seem to end up by merely studying the subject's *thoughts* — which are only another collection of
objects. Modern psychology, for example, that purports
to study both conscious and unconscious man, has in fact
only constructed complicated patterns from men's
thoughts, and called it psychology. So it seems to have

veered away from its original aim, and has constructed yet another pattern of *objects*. Even Descartes, who started well with his original statement 'I think', veered off almost immediately to a study of the thoughts he was thinking and the objects he was thinking about.

It is possible that human knowledge is of itself a constant 'objectifying' process and any attempt to study subjects will end up as a definition of objects. But it is also possible that it is not.

The matter eludes us, and language, our most complete way of knowing to date, puts up barriers and blocks our way with fixed patterns. Grammar, however, may help us out. A complete grammatical sentence, curiously enough, consists of a *subject*, a verb and an *object*. If the sentence is intransitive it will have no object but it still requires a verb, as in the sentences 'she smiles'. So the verb may help us understand subjects in much the way that adjectives help us describe objects. We should possibly pay more attention to verbs, or break down grammar altogether. But as we still do not know how to deal with subjects, I shall in discussing the *man/ man* relationship, be moving blindly.

With this difficulty ahead, I now turn to those areas of thought where the relation of man to man is most apparent: philosophy, theology and society — to follow the changing relationships in these areas during the later Middle Ages.

*   *   *

During the early and high Middle Ages there was little philosophy in the modern or Greek sense. Thought was dominated by a vast body of theology outside the scope of an individual mind, and original thinkers were largely limited to the fringe task of commenting on a world that was more mysterious and complex than any one man could fully comprehend. However, commentators gradually gained confidence and developed into original organisers of thought. In the thirteenth century some considerable thinkers appeared, and St. Thomas Aquinas in that century took the important step of presenting, under the controlling intelligence of one mind, an analysis of the whole universe and of all existing branches of thought. There are indications that at the end of his life St. Thomas was horrified at what he had done, but whatever his ultimate purpose, it was an important achievement. It was the beginning of individual philosophers: one controlling and reasoning mind could grasp the whole corpus of universal knowledge, and knowledge began, correspondingly, to be sifted through the net of the individual thinker. The following centuries saw the rise of a number of independent philosophers and theologians, who pitched their own minds against the body of accepted theological thought.

I shall deal here with only one of the controversies that occupied the philosophers of the later Middle Ages, the one that most centrally affected the change from medieval into modern thought: the 14th century controversy between the Realists and the Nominalists concerning the nature of form.

The accepted traditional view was that forms — the universal Platonic and Aristotelian forms inherited from the Greeks — actually exist as things. A universal is not a generalisation or abstraction, it is a thing or *res;* it has thinginess, or as we would say, it is 'real'. The form *tree* is real, it is not just a common name given to a number of tall plants.

This view of a universal as a *thing* is hard for us to understand. It indicates that the universal form, in the medieval experience, was a 'real' physical thing, and that the medieval cosmos is made up of 'real' universal forms.

The new philosophers of the fourteenth century questioned this view. They thought that a form or Idea is only a name, a *nomen* — it is purely an abstract concept, and has no thinginess or 'reality'. Individual trees exist, but the concept 'tree' is only an abstraction. In other words, universals have no reality, they are only names given to groups of similar objects.

Thus began the great controversy between the traditional 'Realists' who said that the universal forms have 'thinginess'; and the new 'Nominalists', who said that universals are only names, and the only 'things' that exist are individual objects. This controversy forged a new word *reality* out of the Latin word for thing, *res*.

The Church opposed the Nominalist view because it undercut the foundations of accepted theology and cosmology; but people's thoughts were so clearly tending in that direction that the Nominalists won the argument in the sense that they completely superceded the Realist view. During the following two hundred years reality dropped from *universal* forms to *individual* objects so completely, that it was almost impossible for anybody to think themselves back again into the original medieval experience.

This Realist-Nominalist controversy is the great divide between medieval reality and modern reality. To the Realist view everything partakes of universality, from Christ and the Sacraments, to the Elements, to any particular form — and every form has cosmic and universal application. To the Nominalist view *reality* only consists of the individual objects we see in space.

This drop in the nature of reality from the *universal* to the *individual* is a drop in the *size* of reality, or in the size of the units of reality. It coincides with the advent of the new individual thinkers. Perhaps it was because the thinker himself changed from being a personification of universal Man, to become an individualist, that the objects of his reality dropped from the universal to the particular. Whatever the reason, there was an open, public, clear and complete philosophical shift at this historical period, in the *object/cosmos* and *object/object* relationships — and implicitly a similar shift in the *man/object* and *man/cosmos* relationships.

What does a philosophical 'drop' in reality mean? It obviously runs parallel to other changes that we have observed. In mechanics we have seen the same change

as a melting away of form in favour of a multiplicity of analysable shapes in space.   In art we have also seen that as
the Middle Ages progress, the objects painted are increasingly defined in relation to space and time, and are steadily reduced from a universal aspect to individual entities.   In the early Middle Ages the figures of Christ and
the angels are more universal, important and powerful
than man.   By the Renaissance they have dwindled, and
have the proportions of Man.   In the 17th century they
are not even commensurate with Man, but are more like
individual men, each with their particular individual
character and movement, as in the paintings of Velazquez and Rembrandt.   And a modern painting of Christ
could not even be worshipped like a medieval one,
because it does not have the necessary spirit or universal
quality.   Either the figures depicted are gradually being
reduced in relation to man; or alternatively man is growing in stature in relation to them.

There was, moreover, during the later Middle Ages, a
noticeable change in the attitude to material things.   We
receive the impression from early medieval literature and
painting that the number of objects, plants and animals
in the world is very limited: there are lions, and roses,
and herbs, and stars and fishes and oak trees — these
recur constantly, each with its symbolic significance.
But during the later Middle Ages and through into the
seventeenth century, the profusion and abundance of
inanimate and animate objects that are painted or written about, increases rapidly.   People begin to name

and recognise different species and varieties of plants and animals. This growing profusion of natural things somehow took away the symbolic universal significance of any single object. We are moving from the world of the One, into the world of the Many. And the profusion of life and natural history that twines its way round much Baroque painting is an illustration of the change.

What was the importance of the Nominalist victory? The entire functioning of the world in terms of universal forms is quite different from its functioning with individual objects. It is the difference between alchemy and chemistry. The alchemist was not trying to make a certain amount of gold — say 500 pounds' worth, — he was trying to achieve Gold itself with all the universal cosmic salvation and perfection that this implied. It was a qualitative quest, not a quantitative one. Alchemy depends on the universality of metals. Even the alchemist's materials, the elements, are universal and linked with the whole cosmos as divisions of the universe. By the eighteenth century this realist world of universals which had disappeared from other branches of thought, finally withdrew even from chemistry. Chemical bodies were increasingly regarded as simple material objects, and subjected to an analysis of weight and quantity. A modern piece of gold only has the properties of the lump that you can hold in your hand; the alchemist's gold had a universal quality that linked it with the cosmos.

It is the *universality* of a medieval form that so greatly distinguishes it from the limited existence of a modern object defined as it is by a spatial framework. It is one of the important powers of this medieval personality-system that forms are not confined to their particular concrete appearance. They are almost personalities with an autonomous will of their own; whereas modern objects are individual things, imprisoned in space. A medieval form can affect man at all times, in any place and from any distance. There is no distance between it and us. It is ever-present, always at home with us.

The Nominalist limitation of reality to individual objects also damaged the working of theological symbols. The combined concreteness and universality of a form are the basis of a theological symbol. The cross, for instance, might appear in wood or stone or other material, but wherever it appeared it was always 'the cross'. To the Nominalist these crosses are only a collection of different objects. Once you take away the *res*, or thinginess, from the cross you reduce the objects to a variety of separate pieces of material, and the 'cross' to an abstract idea. This removes most of its power and truth. It is the beginning of a split: the external world of matter and 'reality' is parting company from the internal realm of the mind.

Following upon the Realist-Nominalist controversy a few crucial linguistic innovations occurred, revealing the new status of things. In 16th and 17th century England two new words come into common use: the word *real*, and a new word *conscious*. The appearance of these two words shows the new distinction that is now being understood between physical reality and the conscious observer. The Realist-Nominalist controversy is therefore the first step to the Cartesian dualism of the 17th century: the total separation of *mind* (consciousness) from *matter* (reality).

This gradual separation of ourselves as observers from the physical world shows up in another linguistic change. The medieval mind tended to personalize objects, and in old English inanimate objects were regularly given gender: we read of the sun that *he* is high, and the moon that *she* is silver. The neutral *it* only started to be commonly used for inanimate objects in the 16th century, but when the changeover came it was so rapid, that by the mid-seventeenth century the use of masculine and feminine genders for inanimate objects was considered merely archaic or poetic.

NOMINALIST V. REALIST (A technical note)

At first glance it would seem that the Realist world has today been entirely superceded, and the Nominalist world is the one we are living in at the present moment. But this is not so.

The perfect Nominalist argument applies only to constructed objects and to space itself. A nominalist can demolish the realist argument quite simply with a constructed object like a sofa. A *sofa* has no absolute or ideal form, it is only a name given to objects of a similar purpose, because if you give different names to various modifications of a sofa — such as a *sofa,* a *divan,* a *settee,* a *chaise-longue* — the universal and absolute concept of sofa as a form disappears. It is not surprising that the nominalist victory came at a time just preceding the great new era of mechanical inventions.

The Nominalist view also appears to mark the beginning of the modern analytical method of 'generalisation', whereby from a study of particular cases general properties are deduced. It favours, too, the technique of analysing down to parts, followed by a reconstruction on the assumption that the whole is only made up of the parts. Nominalism introduces us to a knowledge based on analysis down to parts, and on 'generalisation' from particulars.

However, if we look closely at present-day knowledge, we shall find that generalisation is not, for all its vaunted importance in modern thought, the basis of modern reality. Nor is Nominalism the over-riding basis of modern thought. According to modern thought there are three types of structure in nature — and they share realism and nominalism between them:

1. The first type of structure is well described by the material physical laws of the universe. These are the laws of inanimate matter. But these modern laws are akin to medieval absolutes. Whatever may be said about the way they are being discovered, the laws themselves are not in any way *generalisations* about similar objects,

because a generalisation requires of any one particular entity that it be different in at least one respect from any other similar entity. But in the laws of inanimate matter — say the laws governing oxygen atoms — the laws of one oxygen atom are identical to the laws of another. There is *no* difference between one oxygen atom and another in respect of its laws. Therefore *the laws of matter* are still, in the medieval sense, *absolute,* and belong to a universal range of being. (This is Realism).

2. The only way in which one oxygen atom varies from another is that it *is* another, in respect of being in a different point *in space and time.* This, the spatial-temporal quality, is the only one in which physical objects are particulars and not universals, according to modern scientific theory and assumptions. Therefore the generalising and building up from parts and individual cases applies in modern thought only to *space.* The nominalist declaration is a declaration that things are in space. But the realist universal opinion is still tacitly the basis for the laws of the universe.

3. The third type of structure in nature is governed by the laws of living beings. These seem to share the nominalist and the realist view of nature between them. On the one hand nature does make a tree always as a tree — but on the other hand no two living things are identical; and evolution has shown that no living forms are stable.

Therefore modern cosmology and physical theory has a curious hidden flaw in it which is visible in the light

85

of the Realist-Nominalist controversy: Namely, that the world of *space* is the world of individual objects; but the *laws of matter* are the world of universals. Space is *different* wherever we are, but the universal laws of matter are apparently everywhere *the same*. Modern physical laws therefore have nothing to do with space. This flaw or inconsistency may be open to beautiful expansion, and hide a breaking point at which to crack open, or free us from, the apparently closed system of modern physical theory and individual objectivity.

CHANGING UNITS OF REALITY

The change in the units of reality during the later Middle Ages is a major event, and allows some careful formulation.

In philosophy the event appears as a change from *universals* to *particulars*. In art it appears as a gradual decrease in the size of the units of reality in relation to man, and a gradual separation of the observer from his system by a steadily increased 'objectivity'. In mechanics it appears as a gradual reduction of forms into another medium: that of space.

So what general event is occurring here? The Realist-Nominalist controversy suggests that it is a sudden break from one system of relationships to another. However, the history of art reveals a sliding scale. This makes the event more interesting. It is possible that, as in many organic events, there is a slow shifting, followed by a sudden change of structure in the more brittle philosophical area.

Viewing this whole complex of change therefore in its full historical perspective, what is the great event? It may be any of three things:

1. The apparent change of units from universals to particulars may in fact be an illusion — in the French sense of *plus ça change plus c'est la même chose*. An example of such a change would be that every father has greater authority than his son, and as generations follow each other, authority is apparently on a steady decline — rather like the illusory movement of a person treading water. A gradual shifting from larger to smaller units of reality, or from universals to particulars, may be an illusory effect of this kind. However, the fact that the Realist world disappeared so completely, and is so utterly impossible for us to understand any longer, suggests that the shifting of units is real, and not illusory. That being so, there may be either a change involving *quantity* and *size;* or a change of *kind*.

2. If this whole event involves changes of quantity, what is measurable about it? The history of art does suggest that the objects of nature and the depicted symbols of theology are gradually declining during the Middle Ages in their relation to Man — or to put it the other way, that Man's stature is growing in relation to them. If there is a change of size, however, it is obviously not in a physical sense but in the sense of power, universality

or emotional content. Such a reduction in the size of units could be due to an analytical method of understanding things, which gradually breaks things down to their parts, and so to smaller units. The fact that the medieval cosmos specifically declares its closeness to unity or totality, whereas the modern cosmos is made up of indefinitely small parts with no approach to totality, does suggest that there has been some sort of quantitative reduction in the units. The gradualness of the change, covering several centuries, also suggests that there is a *scale of change* here which is somehow measurable.

So if we took man as a stable factor we might be able to construct a scale where the units of reality vary in relation to him. But the evidence we have, tells us that man does not just alter in stature in relation to the world. He himself is becoming something different in *kind:* He is changing from a personification of Man, to becoming an individual; he is now more 'objective', and so on. Therefore the change is not only in the units of reality but in the whole *man/cosmos* relationship itself. Consequently there is no external or stable factor against which to measure the change, so that we must discard a quantitative view of the problem and turn to the third possibility.

3. The third possibility is that there is a gradual change in the *man/cosmos* relationship — and by implication in the other four relationships — whereby at each stage the relationship stands in a pattern different

from the pattern at any other stage. But if this is so, how can we understand a scale whose units vary totally in kind at different points, when the scale does not possess any external framework of reality against which to compare the patterns — this framework having been excluded in the previous paragraph?

* * *

We are blocked from any further generalities on the matter, and must therefore turn to the events themselves, and try to extract further clues from the particular case before us.

In this particular group of events (which I shall sometimes call the medieval-to-modern sliding scale) we can certainly detect an analytical method operating. It seems that, throughout this whole period of history, information about the world is being analysed, and methods of thinking about it are being used which seem to determine the actual pattern of knowledge that ensues. One example of analysis is the medieval reduction of a multiplicity of objects to four simple elements; another example is the modern analysis of matter by weight into a greater number of elements. These are two different methods of analysis. A further example of analysis, and the most notable one here, is an increasing objectivity, which consists of analysing an object's relation to the observer, and deciding what belongs to the external world and what belongs to the internal spirit; or distinguishing what is believed to pertain to God from what is thought to be associated with Man. Probably yet another example of analysis is the reduction of universal forms down to particular objects.

These gradual distinctions and increasing definitions seem to determine at every stage the particular system of knowledge that each century will construct.

The analysis is of two kinds: there is *analysis of material,* and there is a slower and more gradual *analysis of* basic *relationships.* An analysis of material consists in discovering more about the facts before us, without questioning the basic relationships of knowledge. For example: the nature and structure of the world are today being analysed and explored in terms of *space, time, mass, number* and so on, and many revolutionary discoveries can be made, but so long as the *type* of relationships themselves — namely space, mass, number, energy, etc. — are not questioned, this analysis is only an analysis of material. As such it is static, and collects and arranges all information within a set framework. This kind of analysis has been proving very fruitful. Biochemistry, for example, is advancing today at a happy pace, without the underlying relationships of weight, electrical forces and so on being in any way questioned nor altered. Astronomy is also making great discoveries, and various theories of the cosmos are being propounded, all within the same underlying framework of relationships: space, time and energy.

An analysis of material is therefore *static* and *cumulative*

90

or inclusive. It accepts and arranges material within a set framework. Every age and every system of reality has had these set frameworks of relationship and has stored its information within them. Both medieval and modern cosmology have been built up in this way.

The second type of analysis, however, which we can detect over this medieval-modern sliding scale, is a very gradual *analysis of the relationships themselves.* This type of analysis is not static nor cumulative. It causes a shift, because once a new set of relationships is accepted, the old set with all its accompanying system of knowledge is discarded, and we move on. Thus, as modern relationships have been forged, the medieval ones have been discarded and left behind. A steady and increasing 'objectivity' during the later Middle Ages — which is an analysis of the *man/object* relationship — caused the medieval units of reality to be abandoned in favour of more modern units. Therefore the very analysis of relationships will cause a shift or change in the knowledge itself, so that each degree of analysis produces a different system of reality.

The *analysis of material* is static and *inclusive* (in that it tends to accumulate more and more information within a set system of relationships); the *analysis of relationships* is dynamic and *exclusive* in that it discards past systems and all that belongs to them. Whereas analysis of material occurs within a known framework, an analysis of relationships, so far as we have discovered, does not, and has no known or external framework of reality.

Therefore, we can conclude — and this is very important — that *material* and *relationships* are two distinct things, since the analysis of each produces a different effect. A general axiom is therefore emerging: that an analysis of material does not change the material, but the analysis of a relationship does slowly affect and alter the relationship, and in such a way that each stage in analysis involves a shift to a new mentality. We have witnessed, for example, that as man related objects more and more consciously to himself, the quality and content of the units of reality altered by that amount. So historically speaking this analysis of relationships produces a shift in the units of reality, whereas a simple analysis of objects does not change the objects. Therefore, *units of reality* are also not the same as *objects*.

In the medieval/modern scale we are studying, these two types of analysis could be portrayed graphically:

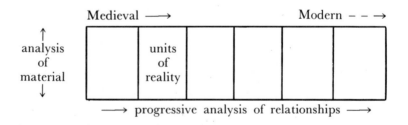

In the graph, an *analysis of material* in any one period of history will build up each column or system of reality, based on certain units of reality. But the gradual *ana-*

92

lysis of relationships causes reality to change and shift from one column to another, from one type of unit to another, and from one cosmology to another. The graph is simple enough, but no graph of this kind has any exterior framework against which to set it or by which to measure it. It is a floating pattern.

Lowering our sights, we can therefore see that from the early Middle Ages to the present day man has proceeded to ever greater 'objectivity' in his thought (to use a modern word), and that at different stages of this objectivity his units of thought are of different kinds, or different sizes. At the most 'subjective' or undifferentiated end of the graph we meet with the idea of totality, of cosmic opposites, of great spiritual powers, and of forms that have potentiality and inner qualities, and a centre and a circumference. As we proceed towards simpler objects, the totality is split into parts; and finally, at the modern end of the graph, we have a reality composed of indefinitely divisible objects that are subject to units of thought such as space and time (co-ordinates fully comprehensible by *one* man) which show a high degree of relativism in their relation to each other and to man. All knowledge at this modern end of the graph is seen as relative to man. Thus at one end of the scale there is a world of universals and absolutes such as we meet with in religion; and at the other end we have a world of relative truths where knowledge is essentially a relative matter, such as we meet with in modern science and modern psychology. But in view of what I have argued it appears that one end of the scale cannot be understood in the terms of the other end. So religion cannot be understood in terms of science or psychology — nor can psychology or science be understood in terms of religion.

We are faced with the problem of how to relate different types of reality to each other. Since our own body of thought lies at one end of the medieval-modern scale, it is difficult to see how our present knowledge can help us to grasp the meaning of the other end of the scale. Any attempt to analyse larger or 'alien' units of thought in terms of smaller of 'familiar' ones — such as an attempt to explain the medieval world in modern terms — is faced with two serious objections:

1)   Firstly, if you define any system in terms of a new set of relationships, you obviously alter its quality and content. Any interpretation in terms of 'alien' units (as for example a statement that the medieval cosmos is merely a spatial system which was centred on the earth and not a system of totality at all, or that their concept of chaos was only a misconception) merely leaves you at the level to which your own knowledge belongs — in this case at the objective level of space as experienced by a detached observer. You cannot, starting from modern units of thought, proceed either by generalisations or by high abstractions to reach the medieval idea of totality, because to do that it is not enough merely to construct explanations with these small units, you actually have to

reach *larger units* and a more subjective or undifferentiated level of thought. This raises the second difficulty.

2) Any attempt to analyse relationships at all tampers with them, and causes them to shift to a new set of units, because an analysis of relationships is, by definition, a shift along the graph. Your very method of analysis will cause the relationships you are analysing to shift in your *own* direction. For example, if you attempt to analyse an undifferentiated object, you cause it to shift a step in the wrong direction along the scale of objectivity. So on account of the nature of ideas, you cannot analyse them down to different units in order to understand them, because by doing this you shift them along the scale to a different range, and alter the content of the ideas as you do so. The modern analytical method is not reversable here as it is in the scientific field, but always proceeds historically and psychologically in one direction — at present towards greater objectivity. This is the great limitation of this method when applied to thought.

The type of analysis which interests us therefore, and most concerns us here, is the analysis of relationships, because it is the one causing the shift, and because its working has not been properly appreciated.

A THEORY OF KNOWLEDGE

From the ground we have covered so far we can now draw up a list of general principles:

Principle 1. Reality — or our knowledge of reality, since we cannot distinguish between them — consists of *material* and of *relationships*.

Principle 2. *Material* includes everything physical, mental, or of any other nature, and is, so far as we know, inclusive of itself. No materials of the universe past, present or future are, so far as we can imagine, exclusive of each other. Everything exists.

Principle 3. Every system of knowledge rests on relationships of *man/object, object/cosmos, object/object, cosmos/ man* and *man/man*.

Principle 4. These relationships themselves are, so far as we have observed them, a constant fact, but they shift and change within themselves. The known relations between one object and another, between the observer and his system, and between one man and another man, are constantly shifting.

Principle 5. The five relationships are linked to each other in such a way that when one relationship alters or is changed within itself, a corresponding change can be detected in any of the others.

Principle 6. The shifting of these five relationships both within themselves and among each other, produces different units of thought, or *units of reality,* out of which each cosmology or system of knowledge is constructed. These units of reality, unlike the material of the world, are exclusive of each other, in that one set of units or concepts drives another out.

96

Example: The medieval idea of cosmic totality with its internal division into opposites is quite different from the modern idea of indefinitely extended space. These two units of reality drive each other out and are exclusive of each other; they are not contained within any other unit or known framework (other than the one I am giving here).

Apology: It is unfortunate to introduce such static and extraneous terms as 'units of thought' or 'units of reality' into any theory of knowledge, but it seems necessary in order to register *change*. The *materials* of the world are inclusive of themselves and therefore do not change in this sense. The *relationships* of knowledge are also apparently constant and only vary internally or shift in relation to each other. Therefore the phrase 'units of reality' is the term I am using to describe the *way* in which the relationships are shifting, as one system of thought or one set of units is slowly replaced or transformed into another. Since the units of reality are *exclusive* of each other, it is they who reveal any *change*. Ultimately, when the workings of knowledge are better understood, it will be best to withdraw the static term 'units of reality' and consider all events as occurring only in terms of material and relationships — thereby respecting fluidity.

97

Principle 7. An analysis of material causes no interference in the material, but any attempt to analyse or understand relationships interferes with them and changes them, causing a shift in the relationships themselves.

> *Example:* An increased analysis of the *man/object* relationship (in other words of the relation between the observer and his knowledge) during the later Middle Ages, caused the medieval system of relationships to shift, and give way to modern units of reality.

This Principle confirms *Principles 2* and *6* in showing that material is inclusive of itself, but units of reality are exclusive of each other.

> *Corollary:* We cannot easily therefore use any of our own mental techniques or known ways of thinking to understand an alien system of thought; since our techniques will affect the relationships we are purporting to study, and drive our knowledge only in one direction, along any given scale of change. My model example is that the modern analytical method tends away from the medieval mentality towards the modern one: and therefore the more we try to analyse medieval thought, the less we can approach the medieval concept of totality, and undifferentiated levels of being. A modern example would be that

by analysing the *unconscious*, modern psychologists make it *conscious* and are thereby altering its nature.

Principle 8. It follows from *Principles 6* and *7*, that it is incorrect to explain away the structure of any system of reality in terms of any other system of reality, and more specifically it is incorrect to explain an alien system of reality in terms of our own reality; because the units we are purporting to explain are different from the units with which we are equipped.

We usually try to ignore this principle, and rely on a linguistic link to explain past systems of thought in terms of our own. But the permanence of language is no proof of the continuity of thought. The radical changes in meaning from medieval to modern times in such key words as 'matter', 'Man', 'space' and 'the elements' must be a warning to us.

A comic example of this mistake has been occurring in our study of the classical world. Every generation in Europe over the last two thousand odd years has studied the ancient Greeks. But each age, reading roughly the same authors, and looking at roughly the same works of art, has found in the Greeks a miraculous reflection of itself. To the Romans, the Greeks were the models of pagan society. To the early Christians the Greeks seemed to foreshadow Christian theology.

For the Middle Ages the Greeks confirmed the whole structure of medieval cosmology. In the 15th and 16th centuries the Greeks were models of Renaissance man, where Man is the measure of all things. To the nineteenth century Germans the Greeks were tragic intellectual geniuses and emotional giants; to Victorian England they were liberal gentlemen. Today the Greeks are psychologically and mythically inclined; and we may even be explaining them soon on a proper historical sliding scale: either projected forwards, or backwards into what preceded them. If we ever start to enter Egyptian thought, we must tread more strangely.

NEXT APPROACH

How are we to relate therefore two distinct and separate systems of reality, and more specifically, how are we to relate any strange system of thought to our own? As we can't understand an alien system either in terms of our own reality, or by using our own mental concepts, we must find other ways. The first course, when this is possible, is to find some existing link between the two systems.

Experience must always be used as a very strong guide here. We are dealing with systems of *reality*, not just patterns of thought. Each age or group of people who produces new units of reality, produces them as facts of experience, not just as logical abstractions. We today *experience* a spatial relation between objects as something that we take for granted and assume to be real. The Middle Ages would *experience* the Realist world of universals, or the emotional content of different bodies, or even a vision of the whole cosmos; and their experiences would be equally real. Experience, as we begin to see, covers an endless variety of 'experiences' — even an abstract thought is a kind of experience. But important ideas about reality are very seldom, if at all, imaginary constructions that have no foundation in experienced fact, emotion, or tactile sensory conviction. Newton called experience, *understanding*. He writes in one of his notebooks: 'A man may imagine things that are false but he can only understand things that are true, for if the things be false, the apprehension of them is not understanding' [15].

The vital difference between thought and experience is that I can describe the medieval cosmos and use medieval terminology to do so, but I have not necessarily *experienced* or *understood* any of it; and I am then only using words that have been handed down to me in books, and until I *do experience* these ideas I do not automatically know at what level or to what range of experience they belong. I am very likely to make mistakes in discussing ideas of which I have no experience, whereas I would

---

[15] Keynes Ms. 2, in King's College, Cambridge.

never make such mistakes about a world to which I belong, and which is for me the real one.

Therefore, using experience as a guide we must try to understand in what way an alien system of thought can be related to our own. The most easy course is to find a clear link:

1) There may be a *historical link* as there is between medieval and modern thought. This can give a great deal of information. We have found, for example, that the medieval system of unity with internal opposites is related to modern cosmology by a series of gradual changes in the underlying relationships. This link has revealed some great working of the human mind.

2) There may also be a *structural link* or a structural similarity between two systems of thought. Curiously enough, modern internal psychology, particularly the psychology of Jung, has a system of relationships very similar to the medieval one. Jung's exploration of man's psyche has caused him to construct a theory based on wholeness, which he calls the Self. This contains within it the various opposites (similar to the medieval opposites). Jung also understands undifferentiated levels of being, both in the conscious and the unconscious. His theory of archetypes is almost identical to the medieval theory of forms and symbols — but with a different explanation. His idea of a collective unconscious is new, and very important, but it may be like God or a living spirit gone underground. Jung has apparently extracted these patterns from man's unconscious, mainly through

102

an analysis of dreams. He himself is aware that the pattern is similar to many patterns recurring throughout civilization. And he has done considerable work on the symbolism of alchemy. He may have unintentionally falsified and exaggerated the similarity between medieval reality and the structure of man's present unconscious, in a wish to prove a link. But he can justify the link historically, by pointing out that as medieval patterns of reality were further and further withdrawn into man himself and separated from the new modern reality, they fell and sank into unconsciousness and reappear now at the level of dreams. However, modern psychology and medieval cosmology cannot be simply identified, since they belong to different ends of the reality scale — as we have seen.

3. There is therefore a third way of relating two different systems of thought: by the *functional link*. Medieval thought and modern unconsciousness present a similar pattern which may historically have changed its function: This would be a link of *similar structure with change of function*. But in that case we are experiencing at present at least two systems simultaneously: the sleeping one and the waking one, which are linked by function but have totally different structures. We experience the modern physical world, with its objectivity and its analysable structure, as our waking reality; but we experience modern internal psychology, with a totally different system of reality, in our sleep or in our semi-conscious fantasy. Modern external reality and modern internal

depth psychology have at the present no known *structural* relation to each other, but they are *functionally* related as waking control is related to either sleep, fantasy or semi-consciousness. The fact that modern science and internal psychology are both being experienced by the same person makes the link between them a vital one.

So now let us combine these three systems, and these three types of link. If medieval reality and modern unconsciousness are *structurally* related, and since medieval and modern thought are *historically* linked, this may tell us something about the *functional* link between our present conscious and unconscious mentalities. By exploring these three links we may be able to discover a great deal about the relation between our present conscious and unconscious psychology. But there are so many unknowns involved, such as the reduction to unconsciousness of medieval thought which is a revolution in itself, or even the possible fallacy of a link here, that the question is not worth pursuing in any detail at this stage.

WAYS OF ANALYSING AND THINKING

Using experience still as a guide, we must therefore continue to find new ways of relating an alien system of thought with our own.

The first great problem is to know how to 'read' alien systems of thought at all. This partly depends on extracting their methods of analysis from their main body of knowledge. We have already made the important discovery that there are several ways of analysing or thinking. And even in a simple study of the medieval/ modern sliding scale the methods of analysis that we have come across are insufficient to cover the whole range of material that we are trying to understand:

> 1) The *medieval method of analysing internally* is superior to the modern classical method in that it knows about levels of differentiation, and in this sense is more able to deal with a historical sliding scale. But it was unable to expand and include the modern analytical method in its grasp — as witness the crash of the Realists in face of the Nominalists. Yet Jung uses this internal method of analysis, and has tremendously extended the range of human consciousness with his theory of four different conscious functions: thinking, feeling, intuition and sensation.
> He explains the whole of modern objective scientific consciousness as merely an over-development of one psychic function, the function of thinking. But by absorbing the whole of modern reality and converting it into one fragment of a dream world, he is not really respecting its status as a system of reality separate from his own. The medieval way of analysing has difficulty in understanding external objects and objectivity.

2)   The *modern classical method of analysing* which is used at present in almost all fields except fundamental physics and internal psychology consists in analysing bodies down to their simple structures or laws.   It is an extremely pliable method as regards the dissection of material, but it is unable to cope with any sliding scale in the units of reality that it produces in its own wake.   It cannot retrogress, (see *Principle 7).*   Classical modern analysis cannot, by its method of generalising, retrace its steps of analysis to incorporate larger units which it has analysed down to smaller ones.   In order to achieve this it is not sufficient merely to build complicated system with these smaller units, you actually have to reach larger units, and a more *subjective* or *un*differentiated level of thought.

3)   The *relativism method of analysing,* which is used today in fundamental physics and in depth psychology, is the one I have mostly been trying to use here myself.   It reduces the fallacies of the classical method, but it is limited in the sense that it mainly sets up a series of barriers and cannot advance any faster or any further than experience. The method is valuable in showing us the fallacies that are likely to occur when we step beyond experience.

These three methods of analysing are therefore insufficient for dealing even with the medieval/modern sliding scale, let alone a more complicated task and more alien system of thought. But we have found that there *are* at least two possible ways of thinking or analysing (the relativism way appears at present to be merely an extension of the classical modern method, but it may yet prove to be a new way of its own). Once you have discovered two methods this indicates that there may be an indefinite number. And this opens up vast possibilities: every new way of thinking that we discover is likely to open up new vistas of being. We cannot, probably, find the matrix of analysis or thought itself, because any matrix we might find would only contain within it a limited number of methods. Perhaps this is a cheering thing in itself.

The capacity to analyse is a mental faculty, the workings of which are at present not at all understood. Apparently this capacity is not limited by subject matter. We have seen that where cosmology is concerned at any rate, almost the same material has yielded two totally different methods of analysing, in medieval and modern times. But we do not know if new methods of thought or analysis can be induced; or if they arise only within subject matter and through experience; or whether they are necessarily linked with a curious thing called fruitfulness, and an ability to expand consequences endlessly.

For the moment our way is clear: Medieval thought was built wholeheartedly on the *cosmos/man* relationship (which they called the macrocosm/microcosm). Modern classical thought has been constructed by particular

attention on *object/object* relationships. Relativity has
been deduced by carefully analysing the *man/cosmos* and
man/object relationship. So it may be fruitful to turn
our attention now to the neglected and invisible *man/
man* relationship.

> *Note:* If medieval thought is made out of the
> *cosmos/*man relationship, and relativity is made
> out of the *man/*cosmos relationship, these rela-
> tionships may have *direction,* which extends their
> value.

CHAPTER V

CHANGES IN RELIGION AND SOCIETY
DURING THE LATER MIDDLE AGES

In the late medieval Church and State changes can be observed similar to those that took place from Realism to Nominalism. The universal unit of the Church broke down to national and Protestant churches, and the feudal Empire broke down to the smaller unit of the nation state. A second and further break-down in society and theology was to occur from the seventeenth to the nineteenth century: a Puritan break-down to individual conscience as the ultimate religious unit, and a social break-down to the individual voice as the ultimately responsible and deciding authority in democracy.

During the fourteenth and fifteenth centuries there was no great change in the structure of the Church itself, but in theology a series of cracks begin to appear which reveal the new configuration that was going to crystallize at the Reformation. These threatening changes are perhaps most clearly seen in the theological work of John Wyclif at Oxford, and in the later national stand of Jan Hus in Prague.

John Wyclif (c. 1300-1384) was a realist working in an essentially hostile and nominalist Oxford — but the various theological innovations he introduced were to carry weight right through into the sixteenth century. Wyclif was a believer in predestination, and held that the Church properly speaking consists only of those who have been chosen by God, not of all the priests and prelates in the church. It is quite possible that the Pope himself is predestined to damnation, and therefore does not belong to the church. This was the first crack: the church on earth is theoretically demolished, or separated from the church in heaven, rather as Gothic architecture has separated the spiritual kingdom from the world of man. Wyclif held that since each man is predestined to salvation or damnation, no good deeds nor acts on his part can affect his divine status nor alter his fate. This doctrine reveals a second split: the *physical* acts of man have no connection any longer with his *spiritual* status. Furthermore, since man's predestined fate is a personal link between himself and God, the individual's participation in the community of the church is considerably weakened, in favour of this internal link of the soul with God. This is the foreword to Protestantism.

Wyclif also finally and openly opposed the doctrine of transubstantiation. He could not accept any separation between 'appearance' and 'reality', and did not believe that the elements consecrated at the Mass could change into the Body and Blood of Christ while remaining bread and wine. He pointed out that this is a ridiculous and undignified idea, has no Biblical authority, and was not a doctrine of the primitive church. If Christ's body is present, it is present not essentially nor even corporeally, but only figuratively. This view shows quite clearly the impending separation of physical body from spiritual Being. Wyclif's method of criticising the contemporary church was to appeal to the over-riding authority of the Bible as God's Word, and to the behaviour of the early primitive church. This 'historical' method of arguing was in part a medieval appeal to 'authority' (in science it was laughed out of existence in the 16th and 17th centuries) but in ecclesiastical matters it introduced time as a new dimension in knowledge. The Church in past and present is no longer one and the same thing — its corruptions and changes appear in historical sequence. Time has begun to take on the long line of a dimension. The pure source of Christianity is being withdrawn into the past: theology is no longer entirely present. Here begins the new Protestant view of history.

Wyclif encouraged a translation of the Bible into English; and he hoped that the English State would help in reforming the abuses and corruptions of the church. A national church, speaking in English, was soon to appear on the horizon.

Wyclif's supporters were crushed in England but the practical effect of his thought emerged later more forcefully in the work of Hus in Prague. Jan Hus (c. 1370-1415), influenced by Wyclif's theological writings, set up the Bethlehem Chapel in Prague from where he preached against the abuses of the church. The Papacy had already lost contact with the Byzantine church, had moved for a time to Avignon, and was now, from 1378 to 1417 split in itself by the Great Schism. Hus denounced the sale of indulgences by the anti-pope John XXIII. He supported Wyclif's view on predestination and on the church of the elect, and declared that the faithful are not bound to obey papal commands that conflict with the laws of Christ. Like Wyclif he advocated the supreme authority of the Bible, and in his own writings improved the use of the Czech language. Much more than Wyclif, Hus was a national leader, and showed by his actions the new stand of the individual person before both Church and State. When the church excommunicated him, his following was such that people prevented his excommunication from being published in most of the churches in Prague. At first he was supported by the king in his attempts to reform the church. But he was duped by the king's half brother into going to the church council at Constance to defend his views. Here he was arrested and tried for his Wyclifite opinions. At his trial he said: 'I do not wish to defend the errors of Wyclif, or of any one else. But it appeared to me contrary to my conscience simply to approve of the condemnation of the articles (of Wyclif) while no exposition of the arguments of the other side had taken place. Therefore I did not approve of the condemnation of the articles[...] I do not wish to maintain any errors, and will humbly submit to the decrees of the council; but I cannot, not to offend God and my conscience, say that I held erroneous opinions which I never held, and which I never had at heart'. He was burnt on July 6th 1415.

Wyclif and Hus were in part church reformers in the medieval tradition, but in both men a new voice can be heard, the voice of the protestant individual, linked to a new civic dignity. Theologically they show the widening gap between the physical and the spiritual realms, the withdrawal of the person from the external community of the church to seek a personal link with God, and the withdrawal of man's spirit from external things. Politically they hoped that the state would support them against the corruptions of the church. The large unit of the universal church was soon to divide down to the smaller units of the national churches. But they lived and preached too soon. The nation State was not yet ready to support a national church, and they and their followers were crushed by the old ecclesiastical authority. However, their new theology was repeated by Luther in the sixteenth century and became the accepted doctrine of the Reformation.

* * *

During the fifteenth and sixteenth centuries the feudal Empire, which held the whole of western Christendom under one authority, broke down, and the smaller units of nation states were formed in Europe. Subsequently, from the seventeenth to the nineteenth centuries these nation states underwent internal revolutions and changes within themselves, transforming society into an organization run by individuals, largely on a democratic basis.

113

We are concerned here with the first of these changes. Many varieties of community had existed inside the feudal framework, but during the fifteenth and sixteenth centuries the nation state became the *largest* or ultimate existing unit. In this sense we are observing a breakdown from a universal imperial social unit to a smaller national one.

It might appear, in view of the subsequent step towards complete individualism, that the nation state is only an intermediary stage in the full breakdown. But we are not merely faced with a breakdown here, the nation-state was actually *constructed* — and this creation is an event of some importance, not easy to understand. The nation state took over the *absolute* qualities and rights of the largest unit or Empire. In this sense these qualities slipped down from universal society to the more limited nation state; as they were to slip down once again to the individual himself. This slipping down of the absolute universal unit is important if we are to understand the status of the individual today.

The creation of the modern nation was brought about by complicated political struggles, and was later discussed and explained by political theorists. Let us first follow the political events themselves, and, taking only one example, let us observe the emergence of the English nation state through the feudal Wars of the Roses.

The fifteenth century Lancastrian wars were a struggle for the crown between the rival houses of York and Lancaster. In this the barons played an important part,

114

and supported whichever side was most useful to them at the time. In a deeper sense the wars were a quest for a strong king. The dynastic split started when the weak Richard II abdicated in 1399 in favour of his stronger cousin Bolingbroke, duke of Lancaster, who then became Henry IV; to be in turn succeeded by his son and grandson Henry V and Henry VI. But Henry VI was a weakling and was deposed by Edward duke of York, who succeeded him as Edward IV. He in turn was succeeded by Edward V and Richard III, all of the house of York. However, Henry Tudor, a distant Lancastrian claimant came forward and defeated Richard at Bosworth in 1485. And in order to prevent further civil war in the kingdom, Henry Tudor married Elizabeth of York, the daughter of Edward IV. As a public symbol of this new national unity, he joined the white rose of York to the red rose of Lancaster, to form the Tudor double rose. From this time on (the barons being exhausted or eliminated) there was peace and harmony throughout the country, and the great Tudor reign began, as a strong nation state. The details of these political wars are too well known to need any further description. But what can we gather from these events which lasted eighty five years, and finally formed the nation state?

To begin with we must understand that in real fact there were no roses in these wars — or rather, that the roses of both the houses of York and Lancaster were white. (The coats of arms of Eton College and King's

College, Cambridge, both founded by the Lancastrian Henry VI, have white roses on them).

How then did the red roses come into the story? Henry Tudor only brought a red rose forward at the very last battle of the wars, at Bosworth, as his own Tudor emblem — and when the battle was won he performed a symbolic act by uniting his red rose with the royal white rose, and somehow convinced his contemporaries that he was uniting the red rose of Lancaster with the white rose of York. The chronicler Hall, writing not so many years after the event, recounts how 'the noble and haute Prince Henry the seventh which espoused lady Elizabeth the heir of the illustrious family of York, by the which marriage the device or badge of the house of Lancaster which was the red Rose, was unite and joined with the white Rose, which was the cognisance and ensign of the noble progeny of York' [16]. And Shakespeare writing some years later makes Henry Tudor announce after his victory over Richard:

> And then, as we have ta'en the sacrament
> We will unite the white rose and the red.
> Smile heaven upon this fair conjunction,
> That long have frowned upon their enmity.
> *Richard III. 5. v.*

---

[16] Hall's *Chronicles* containing the History of England, originally entitled *The Union of the two noble and illustre families of Lancaster and York*. 1548, p. 3.

116

Future ages have followed and believed this deceptive account.

How could Henry VII have pretended that the wars were about roses at all, and to such an extent that they have been called the Wars of the Roses ever since? It seems that Henry pulled a very fast trick by using a symbolic language that was understood by his contemporaries.

We have to understand the use of devices and badges during this period. These wars consisted of sporadic battles in which first one side and then the other was defeated. The fortunes of each king were largely governed by the changing loyalties of the barons, of whom Warwick the Kingmaker was the most notorious. Many barons had private armies of their own, and put them at the service of whichever cause was most favourable to themselves. Each nobleman had his own coat of arms and heraldic devices, and these were worn by all his retainers and soldiers to enable the men to recognise each other on the battle field. The fifteenth century saw the high watermark of heraldic badges. These devices became so important that they were treated as practically synonimous with the people they represented. The political slogans of the period are couched in heraldic terms. The battle of Banbury Field was largely decided by the appearance of the white bear, and the cry 'A Warwick! a Warwick!' Percy's *Reliques* contain poems of the period written in heraldic terms. In 'Lady Bessy',

a poem about the future wife of Henry VII, we read of
some noblemen that

> thus they provided in the winter time
> their councel to keep all three,
> the Earl wrought by prophecy
> he would not abide in London truly,
>
> and in the suburbs without the City
> an old Inn chosen hath he,
> & drew an Eagle upon the entry
> that the western men might know where to lie.

The eagle's foot was the badge of the Stanleys. The
Royal family, too, had its badges — there were a large
number of different royal devices. The white rose was a
royal device belonging to both the houses of York and
Lancaster, and in this sense was of small importance.
The House of York had the special symbol of the golden
sun. Shakespeare correctly opens *Richard III* with the
lines:

> Now is the winter of our discontent
> Made glorious summer by this sun of York

Moreover each king tended to use a particular badge
or set of badges belonging to himself personally. Richard III had the badge of a white Boar. A man was
hanged and drawn during his reign for a rhyme which
was laid to his charge:

118

> The cat, the rat, and Lovell our dog,
> Ruleth all England under a hog [17].

The first line refers to three of Richard's ministers: Catesby, Ratclyf and Lovell. Shakespeare refers to the same device when he tells Henry:

> Sleep, Richmond, sleep in peace, and wake in joy;
> Good angels guard thee from the boar's annoy.
> *Richard III. 5. iii.*

In all the contemporary rhymes and heraldic devices that I have met I have found no specific mention of the red Rose, either as a special emblem of the house of Lancaster or as a rallying point for its supporters. It is officially listed as a minor royal device belonging to both houses, which in itself suggests that it had no particular significance for either. In the political area there is no mention of a red rose until the battle of Bosworth — or rather, in the manuscripts written afterwards describing this battle. What then is the significance of Henry's action in joining the two opposing factions in terms of a red and white rose?

The amazing fact is that the whole imagery of the white and red rose appears during these wars not on the political scene, but among the alchemists. The full meaning of the red and white rose is explained in the

---

[17] *The New Chronicles of England and France*, by Robert Fabyan, London 1811, p. 672 (first ed. 1516).

alchemical texts of the period. There was considerable alchemical activity in England during the fifteenth century, and several of the most famous English alchemists belong to this time. (A collection of their writings was made by Elias Ashmole in his *Theatrum Chemicum Britannicum*, 1652). These fifteenth century English alchemists are particularly interested in the double rose, and in uniting the red and the white.

Alchemy, as we know, was a quest to find the philosopher's stone, or the quintessential gold or heavenly elixir. Among the complicated procedures described at this time, the English alchemists say that you must take the black base or chaotic prime matter, and whiten it. This is the way of achieving the white feminine principle, often called by them the white queen. Then, they say, you must extract or draw out of this white principle a new red masculine principle. This they often called the red king. Finally, they say, you must unite the white queen and the red king in perfect marriage and you will achieve the philosopher's stone or heavenly elixir.

The following is a contemporary description of the process by the well known alchemist George Ripley who was addressing his words to Edward IV. (Notice that all comes out of 'one Thing'. This is the medieval unity):

> And one great secret right needful it is to know,
> That though the *Philosophers* speak plurally,
> All is but one Thing, ye may me trowe [trust],
> In kind, which is our Base principally,
> Whereof doth spring both White and Red naturally;

And yet the White must come first of the Red:
Which thing is not wrought manually,
But naturally, Craft helping out of our Lead.

In the Recapitulation of his *Twelve Gates* Ripley also tells us 'Where the *Red Man* and the *White Woman* be made one' and later on he explains a process more fully (using the symbolism of the four quarters or elements, the four opposite directions, and the rotation and eclipse of the sun and moon):

Three of the Wife and one of the Man then must thou
[take,
And the less of the Spirits there be in the dispen-
[sation,
The rather thy *Calcination* for certain shall thou make
Then forth into the North proceed by obscuration:
Of the *Red Man* and his *White Wife* called Eclipsation:
Losing them and altering betwixt Winter and
[Vere,
Into Water turning Earth dark and nothing
[clear.

Ripley was writing before the battle of Bosworth, and before the appearance of Henry Tudor, yet he was talking of uniting the red Man and his white Wife.

Alchemists were mainly working in the field of chemistry, but alchemy like much of medieval thought exists and functions by 'correspondences'. The alchemist imagined that everything taking place in his alembics and retorts was parallel to both cosmic events and political

121

events. The growth of the philosopher's stone was referred to as the birth of the new King, and it is the king's fate which we follow through the various alchemical stages. So there was a conscious parallel in alchemy between the alchemical materials in the laboratory, the events of the whole cosmos (the red and white are also the sun and moon, or gold and silver), the political events of a kingdom, and the adventures of one man, the microcosm, or King — all combined in the philosopher's stone or elixir.

For some reason or other the English alchemists of the fifteenth century not only interpreted their alchemy in royal terms, but actually got it mixed up with contemporary politics. They address their work to the king: they even believe that the king is listening to them and will follow their advice. They advise him not to waste his money fighting in France (this was the latter period of the Hundred Years' War); and at other times they complain that the king has imprisoned them. Some of these things may have been factually true — some kings may have imprisoned alchemists and suspected them as coiners or even magicians. But if we remember that the king is, for the alchemist, also the philosopher's stone in its various stages, we realise that when they address the king and watch his actions and progress, they are also describing the alchemical experiment itself. Here is an extract from *George Ripley unto King Edward the Fourth*. Ripley is promising to tell the king alchemical secrets:

122

Once to your Lordship such things I did promise,
What time ye did command to send unto me;
And since that I wrote in full secret wise,
Unto your Grace from the University
Of Louvain, when God fortuned me by Grace to see
Greater secrets and much more profit,
Which only to you I will disclose to be:
That is to say the great *Elixirs* both Red and White [...]

By mouth also this precious secret most of delight,
How may be made Elixirs Red and White,
Plain unto your Highness it shall declared be [18].

Alchemists were telling the king what he should do, and Henry VII was the first to follow their views.

The connection between symbolic badges and alchemical symbols was commonly accepted at this time, and was not limited to the fantasy of the alchemists themselves. Shakespeare's *Richard III* is permeated with a mixture of alchemical, heraldic and political symbols. The references to the black toad and beetle (Richard himself) are very close to alchemy — this is the dark old base out of which the new principle and young king will arise. Clarence's dream of riches and pearls under the sea is also alchemical. And his diving down into a butt of malmsey is death by dissolution. There is clearly, in the mind of the fifteenth and sixteenth century, a feeling that the State has a personality of its own, with its own complex internal struggles and psychological conflicts

---

[18] Elias Ashmole: *Theatrum Chemicum Britannicum*, p. 109.

somehow expressed in the king, and all resting upon the king.

What then is the political importance of Henry's act in uniting the red and the white rose? The only contemporary information we have is that of the alchemists. According to them the red and white principles are opposites, but nevertheless belong together. The red is to be created after the white, and if these opposites can be harmoniously united, they will form the complete and perfect whole, or philosopher's stone.

Alchemists explain why the white rose must rest inside the red — as Henry Tudor was later to arrange them in the Tudor double rose. Norton, writing in 1477 during the reign of Edward IV, gives us an exact description of what the Tudor rose was later to be — and explains why it has this particular form:

> Common Philosophy the cause doth disclose,
> Why cold is within and red without the Rose:
> *Anaxagoras* said in his *Conversations natural*
> Inward and Outward be contrary in things all,
> Which is true except such things as be
> Of little composition, and nigh simplicity [19].

This passage is so concise that we must follow it two lines at a time:

> Common Philosophy the cause doth disclose,
> Why cold is within and red without the Rose:

---

[19] Ashmole, p. 67.

The common philosophy he refers to is the commonly accepted medieval Aristotelian physics. Norton is working on the assumption that the Rose is a pattern of the whole cosmos. Cold things, such as earth and water tend to contract naturally in towards the centre, whereas hot things, air and fire, tend to expand up and out towards the circumference. The rose therefore has the white or cold inside tending towards the centre, and the red or hot outside belonging at the circumference. In replacing 'white' by 'cold' Norton makes his meaning perfectly clear. Tending as these do in opposite cosmic directions, towards the hidden inner and towards the open outer parts of the body, the two principles are opposite in a cosmic sense, yet both are contained in the one world or rose. Hence the meaning of the next two lines:

> *Anaxagoras* said in his *Conversations natural*
> Inward and Outward be contrary in all things,

But this raises the problem that the two forces, being opposites, are likely to be really contrary, and struggle or quarrel with each other and ultimately separate. This struggle and division is a feature of the elements unless they are held together in a really firm whole. Now a *composite* thing, we are told, tends to disintegrate, but a *simple* form cannot disintegrate for the obvious reason that the simple form is itself an indivisible entity. All this tallies with medieval theory. Norton points out that the rose holds the two opposite and apparently contrary principles within it, and these do not quarrel with each other because the form they are contained in — the rose itself — is *simple* and therefore firm, whole, and absolutely indissoluble. This is one of the adjectives repeatedly used about the heavens and about the philosopher's stone: that it is *simple* and therefore pure, unchanging and stable. The heavens are simple by virtue of their not containing any of the four opposing elements in them. The philosopher's stone is more completely a whole through its *union* of the opposites within itself. This is the full meaning of Norton's last lines:

> Inward and Outward be contrary in things all,
> Which is true except such things as be
> Of little composition, and nigh simplicity.

The parallel between the rose and the medieval cosmos could not be clearer nor more intentional. At the same time the parallel between the rose and the whole English nation lies just as close to the alchemists' meaning. (It is interesting to note that in this passage we are presented with an inward and an outward contained within the same over-all body of the cosmos. In two hundred years these two cosmic forces are going to separate and lead in very different directions: the outward is going to lead out to the physical reality of the heavens, the inward is going to withdraw into the introspection of the mind — they will part company with Descartes, having lost perhaps their simple unity, and entering into the struggle of composite things).

Alchemists have therefore described the marrying of the white queen with the red king and the forming of the double Tudor rose, before that event occurred. They explain that this union would achieve a simple and stable form. They explained all this before the red rose had even appeared on the political scene, and before any such political union could be envisaged. The stability they describe seems to indicate the stability of a future kingdom or nation state. The similarity of the Tudor double rose with an alchemical symbol for the philosopher's stone is confirmed by a German manuscript of the sixteenth century in the British Museum [20], which portrays the philosopher's stone as a double rose with a gold centre, an inner row of white petals and an outer row of red petals. This is identical to the double rose of the Tudors.

The political side of the symbolism seems to have developed more slowly, and was possibly not quite an invention of Henry VII. There is a contemporary description of the battle of Bosworth in the Chronicle of Croyland Abbey, which pictures blood appearing like a red rose inside the mouth of the white boar (Richard III) [21]. This is apparently the first known refer-

---

[20] Reproduced by Jung in his book on alchemy.
[21] Quoted by Sir James H. Ramsay in *Lancaster and York: a century of English history*. Oxford, 1892.

ence to the red rose. The imagery was repeated a hundred years later in reference to the blood spilled by Edward IV:

> But *York,* by his attempt hath overthrown
> All the best glory wherein England stood;
> And did his state by her undoing win:
> And was, though white without, yet red within [22].

* * *

What interpretation are we then to give to these events? If we were to ask an alchemist to explain their political meaning, he would probably say that the rise of the Lancastrians from within the house of York was the emergence of a new masculine and therefore red principle. At first this event took place under the guise of an internal revolt against accepted authority — both houses living under the royal white rose. The civil war reduced the old order to chaos, and a melting down to levels where opposites meet and new forms take shape. With the appearance of Henry Tudor the red principle emerged in its own colours, as a distinct new force that was now fully formed, and must be accepted as an equal with the white principle of York. This led immediately to the correct harmony; and by marrying Elizabeth of York, Henry joined the red and the white, the old and the new,

---

[22] From Samuel Daniel's *Civil Wars.* On Edward IV, p. 212. In Cambridge University Library, (1595-7).

128

and moulded them together into a national unity, creating the nation state as a new *simple* form like a small model of the cosmos itself.

If, on the other hand, we were to ask a contemporary politician to interpret the events, he would probably say that Henry VII simply used the language of devices and symbols to justify his claim to the throne. It was a masterful stroke on his part to introduce a red rose and join it to the white, because by this means the various devices and badges of the nobles were subjected to a double rose that contained all the opposing factions within it. Henry's cleverness was to use a symbol that popular imagination could sense to have authoritative and cosmic associations, grounded in medieval philosophy.

What is interesting from our point of view is that the double rose on which the Tudor state seemed to build its peace and prosperity is the symbol of the whole cosmos. This suggests that the Tudor state is a type of *medieval* structure — as though the medieval cosmic unity had dropped one level into the smaller unit of the nation state. Therefore this state is not a modern state. With its exact parallel in the medieval cosmos, its centre and circumference, its simple form, and its joining of the opposites, the double rose is an *internal* and containing symbol, and has an internal structure. Thus the new form of the Tudor state belonged, in part at least, to the same internal world that we have met with so often in medieval thought. In that sense the Tudor state could be called a unity which was not 'composite', in a way that a modern social state or organisation cannot.

Since several nation states were created in Europe around this time, it is possible that the Tudor double rose indicates a type of social development and activity which we today know nothing about. But we have to account for the extraordinary fact that the Tudor state was able, within fifty years, to transfer the whole body of religion from the Catholic Church onto itself. So it must in some ways have become a unit comparable, in however vague a sense, to a church.

The Tudor state and the Anglican church stand half way between medieval universal Christianity, and the later individualistic democratic society. This is perhaps why in England Protestantism came in two stages: first in a national form, as the Anglican church (a small version of the universal church) and later, in the 17th century, with complete individualism and puritanism.

Since the Tudor rose, as a model of the cosmos, is a containing symbol, it pictures the Tudor state partly as a feminine and protective body. During the later Middle Ages a large number of *containing* symbols appear in various branches of thought. It is possible that a threatening boundary was beginning to appear between what is contained and *safe,* and what is outside and dangerous: new outside forces were threatening and immanent. It is almost as though the mandorla that encircled and protected Christ in earlier paintings, has given way to a

130

new mandorla protecting man — it is he who is building something semi-divine, and needs a protection.

These protecting symbols appear in great number from the thirteenth century onwards, with the cult of the Virgin whose protective cloak was said to encompass all mankind. The pictures of the unicorn in an enclosed garden is one such series. Renaissance alchemy used a large number of containing symbols: towers, towns, retorts, heavens, gardens.

Medieval and Renaissance gardens were usually enclosed intimate private areas, often with a central fountain or statue — and they were frequently used to illustrate alchemical texts. During the fifteenth and sixteenth centuries the new nation state was incorporated into this symbolism, and we meet with comparisons between the state and a garden:

> Wherefore I liken England to a garden,
> Which that hath been overgrown many year
> With weeds, which must be mown down plain.
> And then shall the pleasant sweet herbs appear [23].

The garden scene in *Richard II* relies entirely on this symbolism. Both the whole rose itself, and the feminine white part of it, were probably containing symbols. However, the emergence of a new red principle from

---

[23] From *Political Poems and Songs relating to English History.* Edited by Thomas Wright. London 1861. Vol. II, p. 269.

within this feminine one, suggests that the Tudor state has been created by a new personality that stands for a time in a protecting and ruling capacity, yet is masculine. The feminine containing white not only remains, but tends towards the centre and is *inward* in the sense of having internal, containing and feminine qualities; and the new red must rise to the outside in the sense of being *not* contained in the feminine, but independent of it — yet held together with it in a perfect, heavenly and simple marriage.

Rather as Renaissance art in Italy held the balance poised between Man and cosmos — uniting and measuring each against the other — so in northern England the Tudor state held a *man/cosmos* balance poised for over a hundred years between the containing feminine and the ruling masculine, between the old and the new, between society and cosmos, until their separation and disintegration into the modern society of the 17th century. England's true Renaissance was perhaps in politics, as the Italians' had been in art.

But the emergence of a new masculine principle suggests in the long run a breakdown of the feminine containing forms of the Middle Ages, and an eventual break-away from the all-containing unity of the medieval cosmos and the medieval church. It is a sign of Protestantism, and a kind of masculine objectivity and detachment that in the next two centuries are going to do away with medieval thought.

In this sense *outward* and external reality for the next

132

few hundred years is going to be masculine. The reality
of *space* is therefore masculine. But what does it mean
to have our 'thought' contained or freed from anything?
Is thought contained in anything? Or are thought, and
both the feminine and masculine themselves, the con-
tainers?

And why or how should the masculine actually have
separated from the feminine at the Cartesian dualism?
Perhaps the feminine was going inward and the masculine outward. But what then held them together before
— as in the Tudor state — and vanished in the seventeenth century? What is this unity or 'totality' which
disappears in the seventeenth century?

The political theory that was applied to this new
nation state resembled the theory of the medieval cosmos
— and they both faced similar dangerous problems
during the sixteenth and seventeenth centuries. The
Renaissance tended to see the State as a formal Platonic
unit held together in perfect harmony of parts. An Italian Platonist, Pico de la Mirandola, extolled the political
state as an ideal form echoing the ideal *Republic* of Plato.
But this view of the state as something *static* (and the very
name state suggests it), was dogged by the problem of
mutability. Political theorists were troubled as to how to
keep this formal unit from disintegrating. The medieval
cosmos had combined activity in the lower world with
stability in the heavenly one, and its overall framework
was harmonious and stable. But the Renaissance view of
the nation state as a pure formal unit had the problem

that it could not justify any change — all political change was a falling off.

Curiously enough cosmology and physical theory during the 15th, 16th and 17th centuries were dogged by this same problem of mutability: how to accept change and not see it as a disintegration of form. Any static view of the world in terms of form is confronted with this problem, whereas a dynamic view is not. During three centuries *mutability* became almost an obsession with thinkers. Here was the sad swan-song of the ideal classic form. We meet it in Spenser's poetry. We find Newton explaining how the harmony of the universe needs an occasional helping interference from God to keep it in order.

The fear of mutability indicates that during these centuries order has declined one step. The medieval over-all static harmony which allows movement and change within it has vanished, leaving only a sort of minor harmony or form, with no over-riding Being to incorporate it and give it life. Platonic form is slipping down from the heavens to the terrestrial level (the first sign that the two cosmic levels are going to be united) yet both the living God and the living man are withdrawing from the external world.

The living spirit is leaving external form, and the outward world has become like a mere clock mechanism. A clock can be perfectly built and set going, but when it goes wrong, or there is some unexpected change in it, who is to put it right? It is only gradually during the

19th and 20th centuries that theorists have conceived of the cosmos and of political organisations in *dynamic* terms.

Absolute medieval form had now therefore slipped down from the cosmos to the smaller unit of the nation state, since the state, according to Renaissance theory, is an *absolute* unit of society though smaller than the 'universal' Christian one. The sixteenth century fear of mutability lies half way between the medieval view of order as organic activity, and the modern view of order as dynamic change. This fear of mutability suggests that the nation state of the 15th to 17th centuries belongs to a new 'composite' order, not quite the same as a pure medieval 'simple' form, (because a composite form can disintegrate but a simple one cannot). It still retains a medieval shell but the new type of order is appearing as something composed out of smaller units. Ultimate order is now increasingly *composite* and the new nation state belongs marginally to this composite order of things: a temporary put-togetherness. Absolute order is therefore descending politically from the *universal* whole to smaller units: first to the *nation state* and ultimately to the *individual*. But it is changing its nature as it shifts, and as it descends from one unit to another.

CHAPTER VI

MEDIEVAL EXPERIENCES OF ASTRONOMICAL DISTANCE

Before moving on to the sixteenth and seventeenth centuries, we must find out exactly what knowledge and experience the later Middle Ages had of astronomical distances.

Their knowledge was wider than we would expect. They knew that the earth is little more than a point in contrast to the expanse of the heavens. But they applied the knowledge to metaphysics, and their experiences of astronomical distance are curious.

If we travel into the heavens with Dante in the fourteenth century, we can discover what can be seen. Dante sets out in the *Paradiso* (Canto II) with Beatrice as his guide, and they reach the moon together remarkably fast, with spiritual rather than physical speed. 'Out thirst for the god-like realm bore us up almost as swiftly as you can see the heavens'. Dante has no concern with the astronomical distances involved. In as short a time as an arrow is poised and lets fly, they arrive at the moon. 'It seemed to me that a cloud enveloped us, shining, dense, firm and polished, like diamond smitten by the sun. The eternal pearl received us within itself, as water receives a ray of light and still remains unbroken'.

So the moon is not made of earthly matter but of something purer, more crystalline and finer. As he enters the sphere of the moon (which is the lowest sphere of heaven) Dante crosses the boundary between the elemental world and the heavenly one, between mortality and eternity. As he floats into the moon he feels as though one nature or dimension were uniting with another without disturbing it, rather as God and our earthly nature were united at the Incarnation of Christ.

Dante's attention is immediately drawn to the patches on the moon, and he turns to Beatrice. 'Lady, as devoutly as I know how, I thank him who has removed me from the mortal world. But tell me, what are those dusky marks upon this body?'. Dante does not realise that a patch visible from the earth would be the size of a whole country or district seen closer to. Beatrice asks him to guess the reason for the moon's patches, and they embark on a controversial topic. The patches of the moon rather worried medieval thinkers — they seemed to be imperfections in a heavenly body, which is impossible. Some thought that the proximity of our corrupt elemental world had tainted the moon; others believed the patches had appeared in divine sadness at the fall of Adam.

Dante thinks that the patches are due to varying degrees of rarity and density in the texture of the moon itself. Beatrice is appalled at his view. 'If rarity and density alone produced this thing, then only one virtue, more or less distributed, would be spread through all the heavenly bodies'. He should realise that each star has its own personality and unique virtue; that his argument would eliminate all these in favour of rarity and density. 'Different virtues must be the product of different formal principles, and your reasoning would eliminate all of these except one.' To explain heavenly bodies in terms of a physical quality would be to deny their heavenly virtues and varieties.

Beatrice is upholding the medieval view against Dante's more modern materialistic mind. But she carefully refutes him first at his own level with experimental evidence. If the rare parts of the moon, she explains, were simply more transparent, letting through more light, then the sun would shine through the holes at an eclipse, which it does not. Alternatively, if the dark patches are like indentations and are darker by being further away, this is also no explanation: because if you arrange three mirrors next to each other and place the central one further back and shine a light on all three of them, the light reflected from the central one will be just as bright as that shining from the other two.

With these arguments Beatrice demolishes Dante's type of reasoning used down below there on earth:

> As at the stroke of the warm rays of the sun the substrate of the snow is stripped both of the colour and the coldness which it had — so are you now stripped of your intellect, and I will inform you with a light so living that it will make you tremble as you look on it.

Beatrice now gives him the divine reason for the moon's patches. She proceeds in the medieval way, describing how God's virtue spreads down through the heavens from unity, dividing or branching down in internal parts:

> Within the outermost heavens of the divine peace there whirls a body, the primum mobile, in whose virtue lies the being of the whole world that rests inside it. The heaven below this, the firmament with so many stars, divides this being into different essences, which it contains and distinguishes within it. The circling spheres of the planets below, by further differentiation, have various powers within themselves, which they in turn dispose of to their proper fertilizing end [towards the earth]. These organs of the world descend from grade to grade. They receive from above, and work downwards.

The power imparted by God to the outermost sphere is sifted down to the lower spheres, working always down toward the earth at the centre, which it fertilizes. This divine intelligence spreads through the cosmos as the soul spreads through our body:

> As the soul diffuses itself through the members of the body, differentiating and conforming to divers powers, so does the Intelligence of the Divine Spirit deploy its goodness, multiplied through the stars, revolving still on its own unity.

140

This spirit produces different alloys by mixing with different materials. Such variety causes the patches in the moon, and so

> because of the happy nature of the divine spirit from whence it flows, the mingled virtue shines through the body of the moon, like gladness through the living pupil of the eye. This is what produces the different lights of the moon, not rarity and density.

Beatrice has described the light spread throughout the heavens as a divine suffusion coming from God and filling them with different effects and qualities, according to the material it melts with. So she has imagined that the moon has light of its own, not just a reflection off the sun.

This journey to the moon is really a visit to the boundary between the elemental world and the heavenly one, a boundary between two systems: the new experimental reality that starts from individual enquiry, and the internal cosmic system that is centred on God. With the bright and divine reasoning that illumines him as he reaches the moon, Dante does not notice the distances involved nor the uncomfortable size of the heavenly bodies. However he has acquired a certain geographical sense, in that he is travelling through the realms that he is describing.

If we move back a hundred years before Dante we find information about the size of the world even more formidable, and the explanation even more metaphysical.

Bartholomew Anglicus the thirteenth century encyclopedist writing in about 1250, tells us of the heavens — in the words of his 16th century translator — that 'the greatness thereof passeth imagination and measure of reason' [24]. We learn that the Milky Way is made up of stars. 'Where Galaxias [the Milky Way] is seen, be many small stars and bright ones and in those stars shineth that brightness. And therefore that place seemeth bright with beams of light' (p. 124). (Medieval Arab astronomers said that the smallest visible star is several times larger than the earth).

Moreover, says Bartholomew, 'this earth in comparison to the greatness of heaven, is accounted but as it were a point; for the earth is the middle point, that therein is great gathering of heavenly beams: and of the virtue and touching of those said beams, cometh full great generation and forth bringing of things that are bred in earth, which is the middle of the firmament' (p. 121).

So the earth is a point, yet structurally the most important point of the cosmos. There was a good physical reason why the earth would tend toward a point. Coldness was said to draw inwards, 'the moving', says Bartholomew, 'is from the outer parts, to the middle. And therefore it maketh the parts of the body that it worketh in to draw near together' (p. 25); whereas heat works outward, expanding towards the circumference or heaven. This is

---

[24] Bartholomew Anglicus: *Batman upon Bartholomew, his Book De Proprietatibus Rerum.* London, 1582.

of course why the Tudor rose is cold within and red without.

But there is also a theological reason why the earth is but a point: Hell is placed inside the earth, in the lowest and vilest part of the world, and it is common knowledge that evil tends to contract and annihilate itself, while goodness and love expand. But there is also a formal sense in which the earth is a point: the earth is the centre or seed of the world, and a seed is not only very tiny, it is formally indivisible. You can break a seed in two, but you cannot divide its qualities; it exists at a simple and indivisible level. A later anonymous alchemist has explained this:

> A Centre is a prick of whatsoever it be,
> Without any manner of divisibility,
> And made as Nature doth well provide,
> So as no Accident may it divide:
> Only by hand but in the Quantity,
> But by no Element separate the Quality[...]
> Thus can no Element divide without doubt,
> The Centre which our Wheel turns about [25].

So the earth is repeatedly called a point, but not for spatial reasons. The stars are not called points, nor is the sun. Bartholomew says that the sun is a radiating body. The expanding quality of the heavens is a sign of their goodness, warmth and light.

---

[25] Anon. In Elias Ashmole: *Theatrum Chemicum Britannicum*, p. 411.

143

The great contrast between modern and medieval astronomy is that for the Middle Ages the heavens are streaming with light — indeed the stars and planets only shine brighter than the rest of the sky because, as Bartholomew says, 'in the stars is more gathering of light than in other parts of heaven' (p. 121). The blue firmament lies *behind* the farthermost stars, and the whole roof of heaven is illuminated, and inhabited by the angels. The darkness that appears to cover the heavens at night was thought to be due only to the shadow of the earth, which prevents all but the light of the brighter stars from reaching us at night. As Roger Bacon in the 13th century explains 'The light of dawn appears to us at that time and not earlier' because 'the whole heaven is illuminated except in the shadow of the earth' [26].

Light had then a very different meaning to what it has now. The clarity and dubtlety of the heavens was not only a physical quality, but also a spiritual one. Light is form, reason, order, goodness and divine clarity; darkness is chaos and incomprehensible formless matter. God divided the light from the darkness at the Creation, and they remain divided and opposite.

Colour itself was thought during the Middle Ages to be composed of varying proportions of dark and light, or black and white. Each colour had its symbolic meaning: green for the Trinity, red for the passion of Christ and

---

[26] Roger Bacon: *Opus Majus. Second Book of Perspective.* Third Distinction, chap. 1. From the translation of Robert Belle Burke, Vol. II. Philadelphia, 1928.

blue for the Virgin's cloak that covers and protects mankind like the firmament over our heads.

As this medieval world gave way to the modern one, these properties of light and colour began to shift. Light takes on new uses in painting, and new meaning in science. But curiously enough it continues to be closely associated with order, knowledge and clarity — apparently for psychological as much as for physical reasons. As space becomes the major instrument of order in the 17th century, light is used to define events in this medium. And 20th century discoveries in relativity have linked light anew with the structure of the universe.

As we have seen, medieval men had no imaginative understanding of astronomical distances. They did not think of heaven as merely poised above them like a high room. As Dante shows, they felt the remoteness and strangeness of travelling up into a different level of reality altogether. There is no remoteness of this kind in modern astronomy. Modern space is the same everywhere. It is the vertical change in strata that makes Dante's journey remarkable, not the distances involved. In fact this vertical remoteness was as effective downwards. When we move down into dark matter, as the alchemists have shown us, it is equally mysterious. These inner regions are equally removed from man's understanding.

As we advance from the thirteenth to the fourteenth and fifteenth centuries, the information is much the same, but astronomical distances gradually become more physical, more direct, more human, and even, curiously enough, physically smaller. Perhaps they are following the principle we have seen in art, that everything tends to shrink and decline to the proportions of Man as we approach the Renaissance.

The *Mirror of the World,* a French text of 1346 translated by William Caxton in 1480, tells us precisely that the diameter of the earth is 6,500 miles; that the sun is 166 times the size of the earth and at a distance of 585 earth diameters; and that the distance between the earth and the stars is 10,060 earth diameters [27]. We read that 'All the earth round hath nothing of greatness against the heavens, no more than hath the point or prick in the middle of the most great compass that may be, nor the greatest circle that may be made on the earth' (p. 33). For what is above is always better and finer than what is below. Consider, we are told, how subtle the higher heavens must be, having the lower heavens below them. 'Well may every man think that the thing that is above is much gentle and much noble, when it that is under is so subtle' (p. 93). There is something delicate and comforting about the late medieval heavens. Of the stars 'none knoweth the number save only God which at his pleasure numbreth them, knoweth the name of everyone of them, as he that all knoweth and all created by good reason' (p. 68). As the heavens are the habitation of the Angels and of God, and hold the many man-

---

[27] William Caxton: *The Mirror of the World,* 1480, p. 90.

146

sions of the spirit, their magnitude is described here in terms of human mansions:

> If the earth were so great and so spacious, and so much more for to receive an hundred thousand times as much people as ever were in this world, and every man of them were so mighty for to engender another every day during a hundred thousand years, and that every man was as great as a Giant, and every man had his house as great as ever had any king, and woods, Rivers, champaynes, gardens, meadows, pastures, vineyards, every one about his castle or place for to live with, and that every one had so great foyson that everyone might hold a hundred men for to serve him, and everyone of these men held XX other, and had thereto great room and pourpris in their manors: all this might most pleneously be received within the firmament; and yet should there be much place void (p. 93).

There will be enough room for everyone in heaven.

The Middle Ages had a notoriously vague sense of large numbers, though they were masters of abstract thought. The figures they describe for battles range at random in hundreds and thousands. If they said a thousand or ten thousand they simply meant, rather as a child does, a very large number. Yet their experience of astronomical distances becomes more real as it starts to become less metaphysical, and more tangible. *The Mirror of the World* says that it would take 7,562 years to walk to heaven (p. 9), and 'if there were a great stone which

147

should fall from thence into the earth, it should be an hundred years ere it came to the ground. And in the falling it should descend in every hour, of which there be 24 in a day complete, 43 miles and a half'. Yet the author assures us, like Dante, that 'the blessed soul which is departed from the body in good estate, not withstanding the long way, is come thither, yea truly in less than half an hour, and unto the most high place before the sovereign judge which sitteth on the right side of God the father in his blessed heaven' (p. 92-3).

In this world, where even the very elements are universals, the practically instantaneous activity of the spiritual world disposes of distances. Medieval man and the living spirit of God can both move faster than space, in a different medium. Modern man believes that he cannot.

But what is happening then to that small word *space?* It was hardly used by medieval theologians; more by scientists. St. Thomas Aquinas scarcely mentions the word. Roger Bacon, his contemporary, is curiously modern in his use of it. He speaks as though space were almost a medium in which objects exist — though this was not an accepted view until the 17th century. The word was certainly not in common use in the Middle Ages, either in astronomy or painting. At the end of the fourteenth century it is being used in English in the sense of the interval or emptiness between two objects. 'Astronomy maketh a man to have knowledge of Stars... And what is between them of space' (1399 - *Oxford*

148

English Dictionary). From this restricted sense it comes to mean the actual distance travelled between the objects, and even the implied interval of duration, as in the phrase 'a space of time'. It was also used to describe flat surfaces or areas in geography. 'Also Africa in his kind hath less space' (1387-*O.E.D.*) and 'Asia containeth as much in space as do the other parties' (1451-*O.E.D.*): Thus it was allied to the human feeling of *spaciousness*. It is in this geographical sense that Hamlet says 'I could count myself a King of infinite space; were it not that I have bad dreams'.

Painters and workers on perspective did not use the word. Leonardo da Vinci avoids the word to the point or circumlocution when writing on perspective — probably because he did not have it to hand.

So long as *vacuum* was believed not to be a physical possibility, it was difficult to visualise extension without any body, consisting only of emptiness. And until a physical vacuum was accepted there was no conception of space as a thing on its own. Even as late as the seventeenth century, Descartes, who denied the possibility of vacuum in his theory of interlocking vortices, preferred the word *extension* to the word *space*.

When Columbus sailed the Atlantic in 1492, it is usually said that he did so to prove to his incredulous contemporaries that the earth is round, and that India can be reached by a western route. But I have found no evidence that anybody in the later Middle Ages thought that the earth was flat. Astronomers knew perfectly well

149

that it is round. If you journey south a hundred miles the north star sinks nearer the horizon at a rate much greater than it would if the earth were flat. As no triangle of vision, or parallax, could be observed for the stars, it was known that the stars are indefinitely far away; and the sinking of the north star was the accepted way of measuring the curvature of the earth and calculating the size of the earth's diameter. Almost all maps of the world showed the roundness of the earth. The elements of fire and air are always painted as circular disks, containing a circular mass of earth and water. Of course a parchment map of the continents would be flat, and perhaps it was difficult to convince his contemporaries that it would be safe to sail round the back of a map. Unlike Columbus, the common mind may not have known how to relate the flatness of a map to the roundness of the earth. But the educated man knew that the earth was round.

It was, however, some time before men trained themselves to think in terms of space, and until they did so they had little imaginative appreciation of geographical and astronomical facts and distances.

During the 16th century the actual astronomical information continues much the same, but by mid century the figures are becoming more specific and detailed. Leonard Digges, the father of Thomas the distinguished astronomer, and an astronomer himself, states that the circumference of the earth is 21,600 miles, and he reckons the distance between Saturn and the fixed stars to be

120,485 miles. He also quotes the view of the Arab astronomer Alfraganus, that the smallest visible star is several times larger than the earth [28]. Robert Recorde, another English mathematician of the mid 16th century, says that the 'earth in comparison to the whole world beareth no greater view than a mustard corn on Malvern hills, or a drop of water in the Ocean sea' [29], and he calculates the distance between the centre of the earth and the fixed stars quite precisely at 69,105,272 and eight elevenths of a mile (p. 156).

But it was only persistent training in perspective space that was to make men appreciate the significance of these figures. During the 16th century a considerable number of 'cosmographical' works begin to be printed. These combine common information about geography, meteorology and astronomy, all under one cover. Men are thus beginning to treat the heavens as part of the *physical* world, and starting to project physical space out into astronomical space. But in these books, we still find great discrepancies in size and magnitude, and the measurements are uncoordinated. In *meteorology*, for example, it is said that there are three regions of the air, the clouds occupying the middle region, and high mountains sometimes reaching above the clouds into the third region. But *astronomically* we are told that immediately

---

[28] Leonard Digges. See *Stratioticos*, 1579, and *Pantometria*, 1571, p. 15.
[29] Robert Recorde: *The Castle of Knowledge*, 1556, p. 5.

above the air is the region of fire, and then the moon (so the mountains would have reached a long way to the moon). On the other hand *geographically* we are told that even the highest mountains are so small in relation to the diameter of the earth, that they do not affect the round-ness of it, and the earth is almost as smooth as an egg or a round ball. It did not occur to people that given these facts the mountains would either reach a third of the way to the moon, or else could not possibly reach into the third region of the air. There was no unity of vision; each topic was dealt with on its own, and unified proportions were slow to be understood. These geographical, meteor-ological and astronomical facts were only very gradually correlated one with another. It was only the ruthless unity of perspective vision that gradually uncrumpled these dimensions and hurled them into space, creating a vaster universe than anybody had even imagined.

For a time during the Renaissance and during the six-teenth century Man was still the centre of this light and inhabited world. The meaning of it radiated in to him, and its proportions were his proportions. There was an equality of status between Man and world, and Tambur-laine could bellow his own radiating majesty from the stage:

> And with our sun-bright armour, as we march,
> We'll chase the stars from heaven, and dim their eyes
> That stand and muse at our admired arms...
>
> Now clear the triple region of the air,

And let the Majestry of Heaven behold
Their scourge and terror dread on emperors.
Smile, stars that reign'd at my nativity,
And dim the brightness of your neighbour lamps...
For I, the chiefest lamp of all the earth,
First rising in the east with mild aspect,
But fixed now in the meridian line,
Will send up fire to your burning spheres...

But ere I march the wealthy Persia,
Or leave Damascus and th'Egyptian fields
As was the fame of Clymene's brain-sick son
That almost brent the axle-tree of heaven,
So shall our swords, our lances and our shot
Fill all the air with fiery meteors;
Then, when the sky shall be as red as blood,
It shall be said I made it red myself,
To make me think of nought but blood and war.
1 Tamburlaine, II.3 and IV.2

And the more gentle lover could still look up at the
night sky, and say in all truthfulness, 'the floor of heaven
is thick inlaid with patines of bright gold'. But it was not
to be for long. The floor of heaven was cracking open.

CHAPTER VII

BREAKING THE SHELL: THE GREAT EVENT OF THE SIXTEENTH AND SEVENTEENTH CENTURIES. OBJECTIVITY AND INDIVIDUALISM

Through the 16th and 17th centuries I shall follow only one event, which is so simple yet so vast that it took almost two hundred years to unfold in all its full and slow grandeur. This event was the transformation of medieval reality into modern reality. But it can be defined in so many ways, and has so many aspects, that every new way of explaining it gives us a new insight into our own mentality, and tells us anew where we ourselves are standing in the great course of human thought.

The event, quite simply, was the conscious detachment of man from his environment or from external reality — the intentional separation of the observer from the reality he was observing.

Man achieves this during these centuries by stepping back and placing himself *outside* the framework of his knowledge. But as he steps back he observes his own previous position in the world, and includes his previous points of view in his new field of vision. This is known as *objectivity*.

As he detaches his feelings from the physical world,

he also makes new definitions about the qualities that belong to him personally and the qualities that belong to the material or external world. This produces *Protestantism*.

In doing this he finally eliminates all human and divine qualities from inanimate space. This produces *scientific detachment* and *puritanism*.

He detaches himself objectively not only from matter, but also from other people, and observes them from the outside. This produces *individualism*.

In thus disentangling his own qualities from those of matter, he empties the physical world of almost everything except space and gravity: So space and gravity alone become *real*, and he comes to see everything in spatial relationships.

* * *

It may be that the whole event should be understood the other way round. That man during the Middle Ages has been gradually absorbing the cosmic qualities into his own personality. But suddenly he finds that he cannot devour space. And at the turning of the tide space proves to be so much stronger than what he has absorbed, that he is left stranded as a spectator. And the backwash of this discovery is such a shock, that the whole of his attention rushes out to capture the expanding universe of space that he has discovered, and to which he does not belong.

His external reality will from now on be defined in terms of space. But by withdrawing himself from space, and withdrawing his own qualities from matter, man has emptied objects of all their unique *internal* qualities, and understands them now only in their *external* relationships as objects in space. For a time there is a struggle for control between the internal and the external systems of order. This struggle occurs at the actual boundary and edge of forms. But suddenly the precarious balance of order between internal form and external space breaks under the increasing pressure from outside, and the edges of forms disintegrate, the shell of the cosmos itself gives way, and every internally structured system is suddenly invaded or explodes — and external relationships rush in to take over everywhere, leaving nothing internal in their overwhelming analysis.

What is this *space* that is the new reality? Man will explain that space and extension are what he himself as *individual* thinker has separated himself from. So the negative is also interesting: Who is the individual thinker?

a) Seen internally it is as though a new man, the individual, is being born from inside the medieval cosmos. First he destroys the centre of the cosmos, then breaks through the shell of the world itself and steps out into a reality made by his own individual and spatial relationships, where he views everything detachedly with telescopic eyes. But if man broke this shell that contained him and stepped outside it, he must have stepped out of it *backwards* not forwards, because he sees the old broken shell of his past lying in his new field of vision. This is objectivity.

b) Seen from without it is as though the new force of the individual mind crashes *into* the medieval world from the outside and breaks down its forms and structures, reducing it all by analysis to his own spatial system of relationships.

If both these points of view are to be expressed together, we can only say that there was a change from one cosmic system to another. The old inner and outer relationships of form were eliminated, and a new Cartesian external and internal dualism was created. So perhaps a basic duality in knowledge remains; it is merely redistributed or redefined.

Now let us follow the events themselves from their medieval decline — all explanations are arbitrary.

* * *

During the later Middle Ages *time* began to carry more human weight. In high medieval thought, Time still figured as a formal unity from the first day of the Creation, through the Fall of Man and the coming of Christ to the last Day of Judgment — playing out a dramatic sequence of great moment, built into the structure of the cosmos itself, and showing varying stages of perfection in different parts of its body. All time was in this sense

158

contained in the structure of the world, and all time is *present*. Before Abraham was, I am, said the Lord.

But gradually during the later Middle Ages men came to express the length of time not in its divine unity but as we experience it ourselves. Time on earth has a more unhappy course: the shortness of our lives, their tragedies and decay, the rapid passing of happiness and our inevitable death. Time was portrayed during the 15th century with the changing seasons, with changes of fate, and as a revolving wheel of Fortune that sometimes raises our hopes and sometimes dashes them, but never ceases to turn in endless revolution. This revolving wheel of Fortune has given us the modern word *revolution*. It was only later that men gained enough confidence to try and control their fate, and direct a revolution themselves.

With this sad decline of time came an increasing preoccupation with death, as in Breughel's *Triumph of Death*. A considerable number of paintings around the fifteenth century depict the macabre dance of skeletons. This fascination with death continued through the Renaissance, and into the walking skeletons of the Baroque.

Time was showing its force on the fragile individual person, but time was also therefore taking on human proportions and spreading out like space to become a new physical coordinate. This flowing of time brought with it a discovery of dynamics in science, and it created Baroque in art.

* * *

159

During the late fifteenth and first years of the sixteenth century painters also noticeably changed their technique. Both Leonardo and Raphael, using the richness of the new oil medium, began to paint pictures resting on a base of darkness. The whole area and surface of the painting was blackened, with only the figures showing out of the dark where light catches the surface of draperies or flesh. Light is no longer everywhere, but now only the ray of a lighthouse finding its way in the dark and marking out the places of things. Even colour is treated now as an effect of light reflecting off the surface of bodies, rather than an innate quality of the bodies themselves.

What is happening? Painters are deserting the daylight and withdrawing into an inner darkness, which is lit only by the artificial light of a single beam. It seems that the heavens themselves have been made dark, emptied of life and spirit, and painters are directing their fragile intellectual light toward this new dark space, to chart and explore its empty regions. Space has been emptied of God's light and spirit.

This darkness that descended on painting was to last for almost four hundred years. It was not until the later nineteenth century that canvases began to be painted again on a base of light. Internal light and external light had perhaps parted company; external light deserting the cosmic formal unity of God, and entering the exploring single ray of individual thought. Light has been captured by the individual in the service of the new space, to

160

explore surfaces and external relationships between bodies.

But we might interpret the event in a different way. Perhaps the Middle Ages had consolidated the world of light and understanding (while rejecting the darkness) and only now was man entering the dark areas which the Middle Ages had been unable to tackle. A great incorporation of darkness is taking place — leading to the exploration of unknown realms.

*   *   *

In 1513 Machiavelli took a more startling step. He wrote *The Prince*, in which he advised an ambitious ruler on the best way to achieve his ends by wielding power with ruthless cunning, absolute self-interest, and complete disregard for anybody else. His contemporaries were horrified at Machiavelli's scheme; but he was merely reducing society to the self-interest of the smallest unit, the individual, much as Protestants were to do for religion.

Machiavelli's cult of individual self-interest was strengthened a hundred years later by Hobbes, who pointed out that mutual selfishness is the only true binding force in society. And it was sweetened a hundred and fifty years after that by Bentham, who pointed out that the chief aim of society is the greatest happiness of the greatest number. And this is the foundation on which almost all present-day society functions.

Four years after *The Prince*, in 1517, Luther nailed 95

Theses to the door of the castle church at Wittenberg, attacking the church's system of selling indulgences. He then opposed the authority of the papacy on *historical* grounds: he asserted the supreme authority of the Bible over the church, and declared that Hus had been unjustly condemned. Luther then appealed to the secular state to reform church abuses, and asserted the right of every individual Christian to free himself from the slavery of the church. He expounded his doctrine of justification by faith alone, independent of any good works, and further broke down the difference between laity and clergy by approving of marriage for the clergy, and himself marrying. He translated the Bible and effectively formed a national church. But Luther remained at heart a constitutionalist, and in the Peasants' Revolt sided with the noblemen and the forces of order.

Zwingli in Switzerland and the Anabaptists in Germany went one step further towards individualism. Zwingli claimed that the church is composed of the congregation, not of the hierarchy, and he established in Zürich a church with no government other than the civil government of the community. Zwingli further asserted that there is no Biblical authority for the doctrine of transubstantiation. He claimed that Christ is not bodily present in the Eucharist, but only figuratively so. He held that the Eucharist is not a *repetition* of the sacrifice of Christ but only a *remembrance* of his sacrifice at the Last Supper – an event which is thus relegated to the past.

Many evangelical preachers went further than either Luther or Zwingli in their rejection of outward forms. They did not even base their views on the Bible, but held that the individual is in direct communication with God and illuminated by an 'inner light'.

So Protestants, in various stages and by various degrees, rejected the outward forms: salvation by good works, confession, religious symbols and images. They also rejected the now external form and body of the church, the sale of indulgences, the authority of the pope, and the church hierarchy. Religion was being withdrawn to an internal and personal relation between each man and God. And freed from any divine significance, the material world was now available to be exploited freely and turned into human property.

The main acts of Protestant revolt against the universal authority of the Catholic church occurred over a few years. Zwingli was preaching in 1516, Luther defied the church a year later, and within fifteen years Henry VIII had transferred the body of the Anglican church from Rome onto himself.

As Raphael and Leonardo had put light into the service of the human spirit, in order to explore the regions of space, so Michelangelo now began to free man's spirit, raising his powerful bodies out of the stone. In effect Michelangelo began the massive moving of large bodies. He drove human energy into bodies and raised them with all their heaviness into the air. Heavy bodies begin to move, and rise up, and twist up and out into space.

A few years after Michelangelo had begun freeing spirit from stone, Copernicus calculated his fantastic and vast theory: that the heavy and solid earth is revolving round the sun. By assuming that the earth is turning round the sun, not the sun round the earth, Copernicus simplified the whole of planetary motion. The Ptolemaic system, with its interlocking epicycles, had become unmanageable. Every newly observed erratic movement of the planets had to be explained in terms of an additional spinning sphere, spoke or epicycle, and the mathematics were getting out of hand. Copernicus now showed that if you take the sun as your fixed centre instead of the earth, and calculate the planets as revolving round it, the planets are seen to move in fairly even and regular circles. By this simple change he simplified all the mathematics of planetary motion, and altered the aspect of the heavens. Copernicus had in fact sent a heavy body revolving round the sun. His theory was one of the most important turning points in the history of thought.

At first people did not understand the implications of what he had done. The Pope approved of his original announcement, and the church accepted his theory as mathematically convenient because it simplifies the calculations. There was no physical proof that the earth actually *is* moving round the sun rather than the sun round the earth — the stars were too far away to use as points of reference. Had Copernicus' theory been proved *physically* true it would have wrecked the whole of Aristotelian physics which depends on heavy bodies falling down to the centre of the *world,* not just to the centre of the *earth.* The church's dogma had become so intertwined with Aristotelian physics that it would have threatened the church itself. But as there was no physical proof, the church accepted Copernicus' theory as mathematically useful, and there the matter rested. Copernicus himself believed that his theory was physically true, and even imagined that the sun had semi-divine qualities. But it was only when Galileo later started to present physical proof that the church took fright and condemned the Copernican theory.

As regards the geometry, Copernicus had discovered the principle of relative motion. He had found that it makes no difference whether the earth is moving round the sun, or the sun round the earth — mathematically you cannot tell which is doing which unless you have some other fixed points or some fixed direction to refer their motions to. You can take any point in space as a fixed point of reference and calculate all other motions relative to that point.

So Copernicus had discovered that the medieval system unconsciously takes the earth as the immovable fixed place, and calculated all motions relative to the earth. By discovering that another point, the sun was equally valid as the point of reference, Copernicus had discovered by implication that *any* or rather *every* other point is equally valid as the fixed one — and every point is space itself.

This was the first step towards the principle that all

bodies move relative to one another, and there is not necessarily any fixed body relative to which all other bodies move. But in a search for an 'absolute' reality it was soon realised that although bodies move *relative* to each other, they may be moving *absolutely* and in absolute motion as regards space. Therefore the absolute of motion was now transferred from the single point of the earth, to all space. Body was substituted by space as the absolute framework of reality. And the whole world, which had been viewed from the earth, was now viewed from 'everywhere-in-space-at-the-same-time'.

This therefore is the relation of modern *space* to medieval *place*. The medieval world rests on one point. The modern system expands this out. Space rests on every point. Copernicus was actually replacing the central point of the world not just by *another* point, as his contemporaries and he himself believed, but by *every* point, which is space itself. All points are now equal in status, and every point is the immovable one: and this is Newtonian space. There is no place now, and no centre — unless it be an infinity of centres to make an infinite volume of space.

Space is not a thing that already 'existed' in medieval thought and nobody had bothered to work on. Modern space actually makes its appearance here almost for the first time. In this respect the medieval world bears the relation to the modern classical world, that *one* point bears to *every* point. This is an important fact, and it will bear closer scrutiny. It means that the Ptolemaic system

166

is one limited case inside the larger framework of the Copernican or Newtonian system: namely the system that can be constructed given the earth as the inmovable fixed point.

One of the striking effects of the objective method is that any advance in objectivity incorporates the previous more restricted and more subjective system, as one limiting case inside a larger structure. Objectivity, by withdrawing and expanding stages, is increasingly *inclusive* of points of view — it treats 'points of view' as its material — but it transfers previous points of view into its own medium, in this instance into space.

This new understanding of space as an infinity of places — which was the simple next step following the Copernican discovery — meant that space itself was now thought of as the absolute *place* in which everything was seen to occur; with the result that Copernicus' discovery of 'relative' motion was not fully appreciated until Einstein. In the 17th century place was merely 'replaced' by an all-over extension of space, and the Copernican revolution stopped here. This restriction in relativism was probably caused by the presence of an observer in knowledge, because the observer needed a place to look at everything from, and he chose space. The motion of the planets could no longer be calculated easily from man's own point of view on earth, so the observer had merely shifted his position into space. The ease with which *place* spread out into *space* shows that the 16th century observer had merely stepped out into space, and

167

felt that he was now viewing the world from a universal, almost divine and all-over point of view. We find during the next two or three hundred years that the observer believes he is looking down on the mechanism of the world like a god. Man the astronomer has joined God in the heavens, or taken his place.

God had been the only alternative viewer to man, and God was now partly beginning to leave the heavens and withdraw into the internal spirit. But Newton, for example, believed that God is everywhere present in space, and in this sense God in the Newtonian world has almost moved down to join man: The human and the divine viewpoints are now the same; the two intelligent extremes of the medieval cosmos join together in Newtonian space. All activity would now be understood relative to the individual and to this underlying space.

Copernicus' transfer from medieval place to modern classical space is a big step in objectivity. Man now realised that his previous knowledge had been too anthropomorphic. The three-fold nature of objectivity is apparent here: a stepping back to a new position; the inclusion of the previous position in the larger field of vision; and the realisation that the previous knowledge was only due to particular 'subjective' assumptions or limited points of view. These three rules will apply again in the next major step of objectivity: from Newtonian mechanics to Einsteinian mechanics. Einstein sees the Newtonian system as merely an approximation or limited case for slow moving bodies within his own wider system of relativity. (This is why I have called the process of objectivity a 'stepping back'). Einstein has stepped back once again, in a metaphorical sense, and brought the *Newtonian observer* into his own system within a wider field of vision. (I shall discuss later, in connection with Descartes, how far he has brought *every observer* into his system).

Objectivity tends to take the *previous* point of view into its field of vision — but sits on its own. It knows a lot about the limitations of previous systems, but it does not know very much about its own assumptions. This is the lesson to be learnt in the progress from Ptolemy to Copernicus; from Newton to Einstein; and from Einstein to any other system that may come along.

* * *

Let us pause for a wild technical discussion: The body of the medieval cosmos has given way and turned into space. And this new space is now the container in which other bodies revolve. So we have apparently merely shifted from one solid volume — the medieval cosmos — to a new volume of space. But if space is not just another body, what is it? This is a vital question.

Let us look at the change backwards: If space is a volume, what psychologically is the difference between this volume and the medieval cosmos? Or, to reverse the question, what is the body of the medieval cosmos in relation to the modern world?

The medieval world is composed of the static point where man stands, plus the volume of the world. The modern world is composed of an infinitely moving man, plus the volume of the world. I eliminate the common factor, and deal only with the *difference*. Copernicus has shown us that as regards the observer it is the difference between a point and a volume: the relation of one cosmic point to a whole area of indefinitely extended space. By that extent man has increased his mobility and his objectivity. But notice that the new *space* is on the *man's* side of the *man/cosmos* relationship, not on the cosmos' or the objects' side.

How then are the medieval and the modern cosmos *structurally* and psychologically related? — as a point to a volume? Obviously not, since a point does not really have a structure. So let us put the question a new way: What is the relation of the whole *body* of the medieval cosmos to the whole body of modern space? In so far as the medieval point belongs in modern space they are structurally linked forwards. But the medieval body does not in fact exist in the modern body. It is constructed on this one point of space round a corresponding everywhereness of God. Therefore the two systems are related yet separated by this point. Each system is only a point to the other. So structurally the two system are not related unless this point is a pivot of a larger and invisible pattern.

However, you can progress forwards through the point to reach modern space; but going backwards you cannot, through the point of space, find the medieval cosmos, unless you reintroduce man there. So the systems are perhaps not symmetrical, structurally related forwards but not backwards — or related differently in each direction. So there is then possibly a fourth kind of relationship here that is neither functional, structural nor historical if we go *backwards*. Where is the medieval and spiritual body of the cosmos now? One cannot apparently go backwards to find out — we find only a point. Going backwards *through* the point we reach nothing; moving forwards *from* the point we reach modern space. So let us reverse the question: What does going *forwards* mean? A multiplying? A disorder? Has the second law of thermodynamics anything to tell us about this? Or is it possible that moving from a 'containing' cosmos to a 'detached' one, the relation of men and women has any special function here?

* * *

At first it was thought that Copernicus had merely exchanged the earth for the sun at the centre of the world, and that the medieval spherical cosmos remained. It was not realised that he had eliminated altogether all idea of place, and of a universe with a body, a centre and a circumference.

Initial reactions to his theory were slow. People wondered at first what the heavy earth was doing floating up in the sky. Why doesn't the earth fall down, since all heavy bodies fall to the centre of the world? In any case, it is ridiculous to imagine people going *downwards* into heaven [30]. These objectors assumed that there still was a spherical world with a centre and a circumference, and that Copernicus had merely displaced the various pieces of it.

The centre, as one of the cosmic pivots, had been violently shaken. Aristotelian physics was disrupted by his theory. Terrestrial physics where bodies fall down towards the centre of the *earth,* no longer corresponded with cosmic physics where bodies fall down towards the centre of the *world.*

But Copernicus had done even more silent damage to the circumference, because by making the earth revolve daily he had brought the heavens to a standstill. The skies which had previously been rotating with spirit and vitality every twenty-four hours, were now empty and still and dead. Objects and planets move, but space itself is still. Copernicus' space, like Leonardo's space, and Luther's material world, is spiritless and still.

Thomas Digges, the mid 16th century English astronomer, was one of the first to understand the damage that had been done to the circumference. It had never been possible to imagine the world as infinitely extended while the heavens were revolving, because an infinitely large body cannot revolve on itself, since its circumference would be revolving at an infinite speed. This was Aristotle's

---

[30] See De Morgan's essays in the *British Almanack,* 1845-55.

172

proof for the limited size of the universe, and people knew this. But now that the heavens were lying still and only the earth was revolving daily, there was no reason any longer why the world could not extend to infinite distances, nor why the stars should be contained in any solid crystal sphere. Thomas Digges published an early work on the Copernican system where he gave a diagram of the Copernican world with the stars dotted about at random, stretching out to the four corners of the page. So the circumference of the world was melting, the structural link between circumference and centre was breaking down and the finite bounds of the world were giving way. The world was changing from a solid and weightless body revolving on itself, to become a shapeless, empty and motionless space in which only smaller bodies are moving. The weightless spiritual spheres were vanishing, but as Michelangelo had foreseen, the weighty bodies of earth and planets were moving about in space.

Copernicus had theoretically stepped out into space, and thereby the actual *edge* of the world that divided the inside from the outside was eliminated. A newly discovered relationship of two objects — that of the sun and the earth — thus carried with it a new relationship between man and the cosmos, and revealed a corresponding change in the relationship of all objects to each other and to the world. Three or four of the fundamental relationships had been affected.

The way opened by Copernicus' theories led to many discussions on whether the world is or is not infinitely extended. But a parallel problem had been troubling thinkers for some time: is there only one world, or are there many worlds in the universe? In medieval times this was mainly a theological and a metaphysical problem as to whether the known world is or is not a *plenum* or totality, allied to a metaphysical question of whether God can or could have made other worlds. The church's opinion was that there are no other worlds and this one is a *plenum*. But after Copernicus the problem of a plurality of worlds shifted to the physical level, as to whether there are other planetary systems lying away in the distance in the same spatial continuum as our own.

One thinker at least during this time tried to retain both the spiritual and the spatial world, each without harming the other. This was Giordano Bruno who in a fit of exquisite thought had a semi-mystical theory about the infinity of the world. Bruno said that where the finite world ends the infinite one takes over. The traditional distinction between finite and infinite was that the finite is *divisible* and the infinite is *undifferentiated,* as cosmic opposites. However, by saying that the extremity of one led to the other Bruno was beginning to relate them as a continuum. He himself was thinking more in philosophical terms than in spatial ones because he said that the finite and the infinite each become the other by *extremity* — which is a medieval or 'opposites' argument. Nevertheless his theory went half way to visualising the finite and the infinite as belonging to the same order of things. The cosmic opposites were losing their structure, and changing into a continuous line that stretches infinitely away into the distance. Giordano Bruno was burned by the Inquisition in 1600 for daring to say that the world is infinite.

Tycho Brahe the astronomer also tried to save the structure of the medieval world from this Copernican damage while incorporating Copernicus' discoveries. Tycho Brahe built a planetary system where the earth is still the centre of the world and the sun and moon revolve round the earth — this saves Aristotelian physics — but he made the other planets revolve round the sun as Copernicus had done. This system was just able to hold together the Ptolemaic and the Copernican theories within the laws of Aristotelian physics. But Tycho Brahe was a careful astronomical observer, and the large body of astronomical observations he bequeathed to Kepler were to help destroy his own theory.

*   *   *

So during the second half of the sixteenth century both art and astronomy were exploring an event in which heavy bodies have begun to move in space.

A series of awkward or false relationships between body and space had already appeared in art, as though the outline of forms was simply going to melt away. In Raphael the outline of the figures is oversweet and delicate, more like a line traced on its own than the dividing boundary between the inside and outside of a body.

175

And Giorgione pointed to another danger. His figures, in his *Tempesta*, are somehow too small or weak, insignificant in the surrounding storm, as though the people are losing contact with each other. But this soft melting of static shapes into space was not to be. Michelangelo had driven energy into bodies and challenged their relationship with outer space.

The Mannerist style, following Michelangelo, now went further. Mannerist art gradually swings bodies into motion, using a driving power or energy inside each figure. A new unbalance or tension is set up between objects and space. The painters start distorting their figures in one direction and then another in the frame, or place objects at unexpected distances from each other, or at uncomfortable angles, or crush them into too small an outward frame — forcing the mind to redress the balance instinctively by making an involuntary movement of discomfort from one object to the next, and from the figures to the frame.

Having created this distortion of bodies by tension with their surroundings, artists next discovered that movement can exist *inside* each body. A painted object or figure was made to stretch from one part of the canvas to another *in movement*, no longer as a static form. This was a favourite effect of Tintoretto (1518-1594). In his works the eye follows the movement of the figure across the canvas instead of taking in the complete form in one still glance, and the extremities of the figure seem to lose contact with each other. When objects were elongated

176

in this way a movement could be felt running through them like a tension. In Tintoretto and other Italian painters the force generated is a violent sensual movement of body. Somewhat later with El Greco (1541-1614) the same elongation of figures illumines the canvas with divine spirit.

Even the flat façades of Renaissance buildings were now monstered by distortion. Sometimes a doorway is built gigantically large on a normal sized façade. Or the façade itself is distorted or drained of life. The static classical forms acquire an internal dynamism. A window is sometimes helplessly elongated, and the middle goes limp, its top and its base linked only by a leap of the spirit from one to the other. Pillars are weighted so heavily that they seem to shrink and squat against expectation, and pillasters are elongated or flattened till no body is left in them. A sort of echo perspective is also set up by placing a smaller pediment behind or inside the main one, so that they pull against each other defying perfect proportion — one always appearing too large and the other always too small.

Mannerist art is the first confrontation between the new bodies in space, and the new space itself that registers their movement. In Mannerist art the tension between body and space is perhaps at its highest, yet they are infecting each other, or empowered through each other. Space takes on a new presence since heavy bodies are moving within it; and bodies take on a dynamic energy themselves, through-currented by the presence of space inside their form — unless it was the departing spirit of man that is moving them.

Painters were of course engaged in the most static of the arts. Therefore they portrayed movement caught or measured in a still framework — movement captured in one instant of time. This is modern physics: movement caught where it can be measured. Perhaps the painters, like a caught bird, were trying to fly loose.

* * *

Man was slowly withdrawing from this emerging world of space and moving bodies. And as he withdrew he placed measuring instruments between himself and the world. Number, abandoning its internal structure, was turning into a continuous line with no centre, stretching infinitely away in both directions. It already had *plus* and *minus* signs, and Robert Recorde in the late sixteenth century was using these as properties of the numbers themselves. John Dee, in his 1570 Preface to Euclid's *Geometry,* applied the same method to temperature. He mentions a way of measuring temperature by degrees which he found in an unpublished work of Roger Bacon. If, explains Dee, you measure dry and moist or hot and cold in *degrees,* you can calculate what quantities you will need to make anything temperate. This is the theory of the thermometer — which was to be invented a generation later. It alters temperature from a system of opposites centering on man, to a continuous scale of measura-

178

ble degrees. By applying number and measurement to the four elements, John Dee has effectively dismissed man from his assumed place at the centre, no longer testing with his hand what is hot and cold, or what is dry and moist.

As man removes, the medieval pattern gives way to the modern profusion of extended units, with no 'place', no centre and no opposites. The elements lose their link with him. Other instuments of measurement appear. The theodolite and the telescope were invented. John Dee makes one of the first known references to a telescope. He says that a Sergeant or Captain of the Army 'may wonderfully help himself by perspective Glasses' — the name originally given to the telescope. He refers, too, to the new discoveries about falling bodies that will soon eliminate the cosmic opposition between gravity and levity:

> great Errors may be reformed, in Opinion of the Natural Motion of things Light and Heavy. Which errors, are in Natural Philosophy (almost) of all men allowed: too much trusting to Authority: and false Suppositions. As, Of any two bodies the heavier to move downward faster than the lighter. This error is not first by me noted; but by one John Baptist de Benedicitis [ie. Giovanni Battista Benedetti]. The chief of his proposition is this: which seemeth a Paradox:
>
> If there be two equal bodies of one form, and of one kind, equal in quantity or unequal, they will move by equal space in equal time: So that both their

179

movings be in air, or both in water: or in any Middle
[i.e. in any medium] [31].

(This law as stated would in fact only be true in a
vacuum). We are observing in all this man's gradual
withdrawal from the centre of the cosmos.

John Dee believed in applying mathematics to all
branches of life, but at the end of this *Preface* he finds it
necessary to justify himself against accusations of sorcery.
Perhaps he had a kind of appalled wonder at the power
of mathematics, and the mysterious nature of the new
knowledge. A Duchess of Gloucester had been condemned
as a 'mathematician' in the previous century, and the
word 'mathematics' was still linked to sorcery and witch-
craft.

Scientists of this period making their new dread discoveries on the nature of the universe felt that they were
either tampering with the workings of divinity or were
touching dark dangerous powers of nature. The work
bordered on mysticism or sorcery. It was the age of the
Faustian terror, of controlling or freeing dark powers in
matter and spirit. Within a few years Marlowe would
be dramatising the strange new fate of Dr. Faustus, who
had allied with the powers of nature and the Devil.
Every great scientist of the sixteenth and seventeenth
century shows something mystical and religious, or else
secretive and frightened, in his theory. The single excep-

---

[31] John Dee: *Preface to Euclid's Geometry* translated by Henry Bil-
lingsley. 1570, p. cl.

tion is Galileo, who worked with absolute commonsense. All his books show a human dignity, a sensibleness, and a disinterested respect for the truth of nature, that make him the only model scientist of these centuries.

*　*　*

So there was in progress a great rift between human beings and the world of matter, between the old system and the new. But what was occurring on the human side? Objective detachment and human feelings were parting company. What was happening to human feelings?

I am concerned here with reality, not with political or social events; but the deepest reality that any person experiences is the particular flavour or mood of his own life, and this cannot be captured by theory. There is a flavour to every age, to every mood, to every person, that conveys the main quality of being human or inhuman. It is what we experience in life and say: *this is real...* But this human flavour, although the most powerful part of our lives, does not appear in any structure of thought, nor in any theories about reality. The only facts of this kind that we have are those that artists have told us.

From what the Middle Ages painted on their walls and alterpieces, it appears that the *great* actions of medieval thought were divine actions, and man was mainly contemplating them, suffering their presence passively. By the sixteenth century man had gathered into himself and humanized many cosmic qualities and the world was the great stage of *human* action. By the end of the century even melancholy had become a human quality rather than an elemental one, moulded by the mood of a man's own personality, whether Shakespeare's or Hamlet's. Did man steal his humanity from the divine, or simply allow his own qualities to breathe as the divine wilted? Man's own humanity was now at its highest, having absorbed most of the cosmic qualities. But during this century man was still enclosed in the medieval cosmos, reflecting and mirroring its qualities as microcosm to macrocosm.

Curiously enough, the *mirror* was considered important at this time, perhaps because it was making its reflections more objectively, or for the last time. As the great divide began, and man and the world gradually parted company, the mirror seemed both to stengthen and loosen its power. Early published English books bear these titles: the *Mirror of the World,* the *Mirror for Mariners,* the *Cosmographical Glass.* Perhaps man could no longer mirror himself completely in the cosmos. Mirrors take on more delicate and fragmentary meaning — like the mirror of himself that Richard II shattered on the ground. Literature and art are becoming man's mirror.

It is the stage that becomes the mirror of the world, and now begins the great age of drama in England, Spain and France. Man was projecting and image-making (which is imagining) more and more of his human qualities onto art instead of into the cosmos — projecting

182

them ahead of him as he stepped back to become a spectator. But either because he could not step back any further, since at this final step he would be stepping into his 'absence' and 'not-hereness' — or whether only as a projection of his qualities into the imaginary ahead of him, art at this time was filled with human drama. Man, as the actor on stage, now turned round and facing the new spectators, put his mirror up to nature. A theatrical quality shines even in the painting of this period. Man had turned and faced himself even from inside the frame of art. Human action had survived in projection, in art, in reflection, but no longer in real life. Man was becoming a spectator. This turning round and facing the spectator, as you yourself are withdrawing into a spectator — this is theatre. And at this moment of difficult weight and balance, the greatest dramatists appeared, Shakespeare and Lope de Vega. A few years later even this acted humanity had gone out of Man, and the next *real* human actions were to be in the field of politics, society and revolution.

During the early 17th century even the figures that are being projected on stage begin to become fragmentary types. The individualist Puritans in England finally closed the theatres; and when these reopened at the Restoration a new proscenium arch separated the spectator completely from the actors. Society had broken the medieval 'Man' down to 'myself' versus 'other people' — and only the foibles and comic quirks of *other* people are exhibited on the stage. There is no area left in which 'I myself' am the actor, I am only a spectator.

The visual artists had found the detachment of modern reality by forming a perspective projection onto the canvas which is modern space. But what is this projection (this vicarious experience) where the *real* person only becomes a spectator? What is the projection of the artist onto the wall? It is not reality. What is his creation of perspective or projected space? It is not reality. What is the dramatist's projection of imaginary actions onto the boards of the theatre? or the projected rhetoric of an actor towards spectators? That is certainly not reality. What is the scientist's projection of calculations onto graphs and pieces of paper? They are not reality. Projections are not reality. Both science and art are projections.

Mannerist art was the most theatrical art there has ever been, either before or since. Having lifted heavy bodies into the air, it next had to solve the unhappy tension between *body* and *space*. This was the task of the Baroque style which now tried to solve the problem by welding body and space together. Light was used by Baroque painters to achieve a unifying and dynamic effect. Caravaggio (1569-1609) reduced the canvas to almost complete night, as Leonardo and Raphael had foreseen, with light coming from only one source lighting up the figures in the dark. Form, colour, figures, are now all subjected to the unity of light. And the figures are not the gods of the past nor the idealizations of the

Renaissance, but the poor and ordinary people of the street. Light is now a force entering the picture from one angle and dashing off the surface of objects. It is *reflected* light — visible only as a reflection off surfaces. And colour joins light in this effect. In Rubens, colour is transferred from the material of one figure to reflect off the flesh of another. Colour is leaving the identity of objects and joining light and space in readiness for Newton's discovery: that colour is not a property of objects themselves, but a property of light.

Baroque architecture completed the union of body and space by taking the classical forms, not in their distorted power, but in their original form — the classical squares and circles and columns — and then slightly pulling them into motion: the circle is pulled into the oval; the column is pulled down to heaviness. Then every shape and classical form is quite simply opened out and torn to pieces, and the open parts are thrown to each other and to the surrounding space. At first only part of a form is constructed — the centre section of a triangular pediment is omitted, so that the eye has to leap the gap. Or a whole portico is sliced into several planes in depth, the central panel set back from the side sections, so that the triangular pediment over the door is staggered between two planes — as though the middle section of it had slid back by mistake. Then the whole of the facade itself is broken down as a formal body and turned into a surface area of space. A long facade is divided at regular intervals all the away across with pillasters or windows

185

but with no emphasis on its centre or edge, and the eye sees a shapeless yet constant flow, with no solidity or emphasis of weight. Or a curved motion is given to a facade. The corners or edges of the facade are softened. Pillasters are piled closer together as they approach the corner of a building, so that the corner appears to be broken down to small rectangular steps, and eventually seems to flow around in a curve. Facades begin to undulate, until there is little left of their static or classical form. Then the fragmented forms and ornaments are made to lead one into another, and their edges are confused with the new flowing facades. Pillasters are flattened till they melt into their background. The outline of a keystone above a window is projected horizontally or vertically beyond the keystone itself into the empty surface of the wall, to reach up to some other window. The fragment of a triangular pediment and a curved form swing into each other. Garlands are placed round a window to confuse its outline with the surrounding space. There is no longer the mannerist tension between body and space. All forms and spaces flow easily into each other.

But this fusion of bodies into each other and out into space was achieved against a very heavy fall in gravity. The columns are monumentally heavy. The mannerist body which had been hurled into the air is now beginning to descend. Baroque architecture is a heavy style. Baroque painting was freer of this problem of gravity, and was able to link figures with more ease and harmony, conveying motion over the whole canvas.

Renaissance art had painted a figure in its full *being* — Baroque art painted the figure only as it was caught at one instant of time, with an arm outstretched, or about to fall — yet in the still unity of a balanced background. In this way Baroque made its final statement about *time*. It could convey an impression of motion, and could also catch a scene at one moment of time. Such was to be the seventeenth century knowledge about motion: that it can be cut or caught in static instants on an indefinite number of occasions — as in calculus, which was to reduce the movement or form of a curve to an infinity of stills.

But architects went further and even melted the buildings with their outer surroundings. The enclosed gardens of the 15th and 16th century were opened out. Even the fountains took on oval or many sided shapes. Eventually perspective gardening in Versailles linked the house to the landscape, and finally even this perspective was opened out into the landscape gardening of the 18th century, where the house itself is seen from the outside, in its full natural setting. And here at last the domain of man stretched all the way to the horizon. Every medieval enclosed form had been broken down, opened out, and fused with its surroundings, making the internal and the external indistinguishable.

This was almost the last that the static art of painting or architecture could achieve in exploring a dynamic world. Perhaps its last gift to movement, however, came when heavy objects were rejected as too real or sad, and a final merging of movement and lightness was achieved in Rococo. Here the interior and exterior of a building are fused in fantasy at windows and entrances. The various stories of construction become indistinguishable. In one of the most beautiful Rococo churches, the Frauenkirche at Dresden, built in 1726-38, it was impossible to distinguish where the dome ends and its vertical base begins, or where the base ends and the outer turrets begin. They flow into each other as the continuation of one texture and shape. Rococo managed to achieve this miraculous blend of body and space, of stillness and movement: each instant poised in perfect and weightless balance, yet each moving on to the next.

But a new art was arising better equipped to express movement. The music of the 16th, 17th and 18th centuries takes parallel ways: Through the polyphonic style, where many voices combine in a harmonious whole — to the heavier structural complexity of Bach, and the Rococo lightness of Mozart, in whom every note is absolute poise, bears the body of the present with it, yet leaps gracefully toward the next.

* * *

But these are extrapolations from Baroque. Let us return to our place in the opening of the seventeenth century. At the turn of the century a shattering discovery was made. Two novae appeared, in the constellations of the Swan and Cassiopea, and at first they were

188

thought to be exhalations in the fiery region below the moon. According to Aristotle's physics the heavens are unchanging, and therefore all comets, fiery exhalations and other disturbances take place within the elemental world in the region of fire. But when astronomers tried to measure the distance of these two novae they found them to lie beyond the measurement of parallax, and therefore beyond the moon and in the heavens themselves. This was a blow to the theory that the heavens are immutable and unchanging.

A few years later Kepler (1571-1630) caused another change of opinion. Artists had already exchanged the circle for the oval in Baroque. Kepler now did the same in the sky. He studied the orbit of Mars which had been recalcitrant to simple theory, and discovered that it moves round the sun not in a circle but in an ellipse, with the sun at one focus. Kepler hoped that he had found a new Platonic order in the heavens, but his discovery of an elliptical course for the planets finished the medieval spheres. Ellipsoids cannot revolve freely within each other at varying degrees to their axes. Therefore the heavens cannot be composed of crystal spheres — they must be empty or else of some fluid medium. An elliptical course also takes away the presence of a centre. By eliminating the circle from planetary motion Kepler removed practically all meaning to the terms 'circumference' and 'centre' — and substituted for these forms free bodies sweeping out equal areas in equal time and moving round the sun in ellipses, apparently

189

unattached. He had destroyed the solid shell of the world.

Kepler was a mystic and something of an astrologer. On the one hand he conceived a cosmic system of Platonic and Pythagorean harmony: he related the five regular solids to the orbits of the planets, he imagined the proportional movement of the planets round the sun in terms of a celestial music that could be heard by the sun alone; he even imagined the sun to be the Father, the earth the Son, and the intervening space the Holy Spirit. On the other hand Kepler destroyed the Platonic world by his various laws of planetary motion: namely, that the planets move in an ellipse round the sun, with the planes of their orbits passing through the centre of the sun; that a planet sweeps out an equal area in equal time; that the periods of revolution of the planets are related to their distances; that the sun is the moving power of the planetary system. These are statements about *motion*, not about *form*.

Kepler completed his destruction of the medieval spheres by pointing out that there can be no region of fire lying between the air and the heavens, because it would have a different density from the air, and the rays of the sun passing through it would then be refracted when the sun comes near the horizon, and this is not noticeable. 'The new philosophy calls all in doubt' echoed John Donne in his poetry 'the element of fire is quite put out'.

In place of the solid cosmos, Kepler had substituted a

freer one. He felt mystically that he had found a purer heaven, more beautiful, lighter and in motion. Baroque, too, had turned bodies into space by breaking down the barrier between them. But there was one part of a body that would not turn into space: its gravity — and this began to fall with increasing weight like a dead force. Perhaps the life and energy given to body and hurled up into space was leaving it, or had been transferred into space, and the heavy bodies were falling again announcing their dead weight.

Galileo (1564-1642) around this time made careful experiments and calculated the law governing falling bodies, not as a property of *form* but as a law of the *motion* itself, describing the path of a falling body at every instant of time. He demonstrated that all bodies have gravity and none has levity; even air has gravity. Gravity and levity disappeared as cosmic opposites. Levity was only a human illusion, perhaps man's aspiration that had gone out with him as he stepped into space. Levity was only the human wish to rise up into the sky. Matter had gravity.

Galileo's next act was to pull the heavens down into the material world. He constructed a telescope and began to study the sky. He published in 1610 his *Sidereus Nuncius,* or Messenger of the Sky, and shocked the whole world by what he saw. Galileo found that, seen through his telescope, the moon is not composed of white and grey blemishes, nor of crystal or misty exhalations as Dante had imagined, but is a solid body with hills and

191

valleys, as mountainous and geographical as the earth. The effect of his description on the popular imagination was shattering [32]. The whole world took on a new appearance as the physical and geographical properties of the earth were seen to extend up into the sky. The heavens, which had always been visible, and previously understood in mystical and metaphysical terms, were now, seen through Galileo's perspective glasses, found to be only an extension of our physical spatial world. God, the angels, and everything spiritual vanished from them — the heavens were just empty space and lumps of matter.

Galileo's other observations confirmed this impression. Through his telescope he saw that the Milky Way is made up of innumerable stars and not of a vaporous exhalation as was generally believed. And he saw spots on the sun, which was an insult to the sun's perfection. And he saw that Jupiter has moons revolving round it in an independent planetary system of its own. The cumulative effect of Galileo's discoveries was to reveal a universe of dark and empty space indefinitely extended, in which various small bodies like the stars and planets are poised or revolving. This is the vast astronomical space that Milton describes in his *Paradise Lost,* with its endless extensions of darkness in which only occasional pinpoints of light appear where there is a sun or star. This is the space that Baroque painters had already imagined,

---

[32] See Marjorie Nicolson's important works on this theme.

192

a space entirely dark, lit only at those points where the occasional light reflects from some object or surface. The nature and condition of light and dark in the world had been completely reversed since the Middle Ages.

With his telescope Galileo had joined the heavenly and the elemental worlds. In other words, he united the vertical and horizontal systems, and turned everything into horizontal space. The medieval vertical layers of reality disappeared. As we have seen, the Middle Ages had always known something about the vast distances of astronomical space. But Galileo's observatious made their deep impression because they were preceded by years of preparation, during which people had learnt to think in terms of space and to imagine the long line of perspective vision that stretches from the individual over to the geographical horizon and out into the sky beyond. Man was withdrawing, and there was little left of human warmth in the heavens when Galileo put his eye to the telescope. By his day perspective space was a reality, and when he showed that the moon is only another earth, he demonstrated what could now be understood, that the material world stretches up into the sky. And when he saw the Milky Way composed of stars, people immediately experienced the vast distances entailed, and understood the world in terms of quantity. And suddenly it was realized with horror that the earth is a tiny and insignificant point in a vast world of extended space; that the world was a place empty of man's aspirations, hopes, everything. It was a place uninterested in his reflection. The Protestants had already warned that divinity or spirit is not to be expected in the sky, and Galileo had shown it is not to be found there. 'Ces grands espaces infinis m'effraient' wrote Pascal — and many others shuddered with terror at the true size and darkness of the universe.

New problems now emerged. If there are no crystal spheres to impart motion from one layer to another, how can there be any effective action of one planet on another or of the sun on the planets, without some intermediary medium? It was difficult to accept the action of one body on another at a distance and in complete emptiness. All heavy bodies fall downwards; how is it that the heavy planets are revolving in the sky? In what medium are they revolving? Kepler conceived of a system of vortices linking the planets with the sun, to explain their motion. Nevertheless he believed that the tides are due to the attractive force of the moon, and this idea comes very close to action at a distance. Galileo was doubtful about action at a distance, and he denied this action of the moon upon the tides. But he nevertheless reached a concept of empty space in the world, quite independent of body.

Descartes, a few years later, would not allow that there can be a vacuum in nature, and chose to use the word *extension* rather than the word *space*. He also rejected the possibility of action at a distance. Influences at a distance were too reminiscent of the medieval world, with its influence of stars on man, and they belonged

194

to an animistic rather than a mechanical system. Besides, if everything was to exist in *extension* or space, an effect of one body on another from a distance seemed to belie the new order and defy the very contacts and relationships of this new medium. Descartes therefore constructed a cosmic system of vortices similar to Kepler's to explain the effect of one body or planet on another by immediate contact.

It was left to Newton to find a universal law of gravitation that unites terrestrial and heavenly mechanics, and explains both falling bodies on earth and the revolution of the planets under one law. But some years later Leibnitz once again raised the old objection to vacuum and action at a distance, and accused Newton's *gravity* of being an occult quality in matter — an accusation that harks back to the medieval internal system of animism, and shows the scientific struggle to make everything external and open. Einstein's theory of relativity has met Leibnitz' objection, by allying gravity more closely to the properties of space.

* * *

In the medieval cosmos passion is the opposite of action: passion means a subjection to forces stronger than oneself. This was still the reality of Shakespeare's plays where the world is a human stage — and the stage has become a human world.

For a short and poignant time at the turn of the 16th

195

and 17th century two great figures looked in different directions and held an equal balance: Shakespeare mirroring universal man and Galileo observing nature, and both wrote with equal detachment and humanity. But within a few years the Cartesian division began: nature becomes inhuman and impersonal; and man loses the surrounding reality that made his actions absolute.

At the Cartesian split between mind and matter the medieval cosmos goes over to the human half, and dwindles into the imagination of poets. The word *mirror* disappears from significant use, and the term 'Man' begins to split up into the Cartesian distinction between 'myself' and 'other people'. What are seen to exist now are merely many different people.

These changes in the *man/man relationship* appear clearly in 17th century art and society. John Donne in the early 17th century could still express his feelings through the medieval cosmos in freewheeling fantasy. He plays with the cosmic image of the circle and the geometry of the heavens in flights of disrespectful and metaphysical conceit that would have been unthinkable to an earlier age. For Sir Thomas Browne a generation later the macrocosm is no longer even a physical reality, nor belongs to the public social world; it has dwindled into himself:

> The earth is a point not only in respect of the Heavens above us, but of that heavenly and celestial part within us; that mass of Flesh that circumscribes me, limits

not my mind: that surface that tells the Heavens it
hath an end, cannot persuade me that I have any:
I take my circle to be above three hundred and sixty...
whilst I study to find how I am a Microcosm, or
little World, I find my self something more than the
great [33].

Calculate thyself within, seek not thyself in the Moon,
but in thine own Orb or Microcosmical Circumference [34].

The world that I regard is my self; it is the Microcosm
of my own frame that I cast mine eye on; for the
other, I use it but like my Globe, and turn it round
sometimes for my recreation [35].

And sinking inwards to internal fantasy:

Let me be nothing, if within the compass of my self
I do not find the battle of Lepanto, Passion against
Reason, Reason against Faith, Faith against the
Devil, And my conscience against all [36].

For a little time there was just a faint chance that the
'I' could be projected into other people — to make a
world of many 'I's. Notice the meandering changes of
meaning between the older term Man, and the newer
term Men, and its generalisation in Mankind:

[33] From Sir Thomas Browne: *Works*. Edited by Sir Geoffrey
Keynes. *Religio Medici*, p. 91.
[34] *Christian Morals*, p. 137.
[35] *Religio Medici*, p. 91.
[36] *Ibid.*, p. 84.

Let observation so far instruct thee in Physionomical lines, so to be some Rule for thy distinction and Guide for my affections unto such as look like Men. Mankind, methinks, is comprehended in a few Faces if we exclude all visages which in any way participate of Symmetries and Schemes of Look common unto other Animals. For as though Man were the extract of the World, in whom all were in *coagulato*, which in their forms were *in soluto* and at Extension; we often observe that Men do most act those Creatures whose constitution, parts and complexion do most predominate in their mixtures [37].

Browne even tried to give the internal circle to *other* people

in mine own reason and within my self, I can command that which I cannot intreat without myself, and within the circle of another [38].

But the new social world of *others* did not admit it, and ultimately the medieval microcosm died away or sunk to the level of dreams. What is imaginary and not real ultimately has no effect on the person and is soon forgotten. The macrocosm did survive for a time in alchemy which defied modern analysis, and in a few mystical writers, but by mid 18th century it was virtually gone. All that survived of it was contained in the single Cartesian statement 'I think, therefore I am'; the rest of real-

---

[37] *Christian Morals*, p. 126.
[38] *Religio Medici*, p. 81.

ity was weighted on the other side and belonged to the physical world of extension and to the social world of *other* people.

Shakespeare, one of the last dramatists to explore the internal world of the hero with the cosmos round his shoulders, died on April 23rd. 1616. The first modern novelist, Cervantes, died on the same calender day. The novel is an art form concerned with other people, with customs and social life. Cervantes in *Don Quixote* is still interested in a hero, but the world that makes him heroic is now a world of fantasy which nobody but he believes in. By pouring the heroic mould into a sequence of social events Cervantes created the modern novel. It is this shock and struggle and even this victory of the fragile individual mind over the real world that melts Don Quixote's adventures into a masterpiece. The book is about internal fantasy battling against social realism.

This period produced four curious literary figures: Faust, the oldest of the four, on the edge of spiritual terror and new powers; then two personal figures caught in troubles of their own and of every age: Hamlet against a family problem, and Don Quixote against reality; and finally Don Juan, created in 1630 by Tirso de Molina on an older story about a man condemned by the devil, yet the most modern and romantic of the four, defying the new social order, and laughing his way into the future.

Likewise the leadership of art in the seventeenth century swung away from the aesthetic and *formal* beauty of the Italians, and moved over to the Spaniards and the

199

northern countries who show a greater interest in social realism. Tintoretto and Veronese gave way to Velazquez and Rembrandt.

A new social and public life was beginning. The change can be seen clearly in political affairs in England during the seventeenth century. The dominant event of the century here was the disintegration of the Tudor state, which apparently still held some formal internal unity, like the medieval cosmos. The divinity that hedged the Tudors did not survive to hedge the Stuarts, and the state disintegrated politically to the Commonwealth of Cromwell, and ecclesiastically to the numerous groups and sects of the Puritans. Power shifted from the king into the hands of Parliament, and religious and civil authority was dismembered to the basic democratic unit of the individual will and conscience. Even after the Restoration of the monarch in 1660 it was clear that power had shifted to the citizens. This atomizing of society was explained and justified theoretically by Thomas Hobbes, who wrote his *Leviathan* at the time of the Commonwealth. Hobbes says that men in their natural state are free, completely self-interested and independent of each other; but they come together in society out of fear, each one to protect himself from the others. In coming together men make a social contract that binds them to the rule of law and society. Society is therefore nothing but a collection of individuals who agree to abide by certain laws in order to protect themselves. Hobbes' opinion of society is entirely atomistic, based on the

200

complete self-determination of each person. His theory of a *social contract* as a necessary way of holding individuals together was repeated by subsequent political theorists: Locke and Rousseau.

*   *   *

The last body of knowledge to move over from a medieval to a modern framework was chemistry, which during the 17th century still defied the analytical method. Although it is not at all certain that alchemy was really about chemistry, nor that it was concerned deeply with medieval cosmology, nonetheless during the later Middle Ages alchemy was certainly the 'repository' of chemistry, and most chemical work was done in alchemical terms, linked to medieval cosmology and physics.

Gassendi (1592-1655) was one of the earliest thinkers to reject the medieval formal view of substances, and expound an atomic view of matter derived from Democritus. Boyle (1627-91) also reached the view that matter is ultimately corpuscular, composed of variously shaped and sized corpuscles which group together to make different chemical substances. His discovery of the relation between volume and pressure in gasses was one of the few quantitative relationships established in chemistry during the 17th century. But modern chemistry did not really begin until Lavoisier (1743-1794), using weighing scales, made a correct analysis of combustion, and discovered oxygen. His discovery was followed by Dalton's complete atomic theory, which conformed in general to the modern 17th century corpuscular mechanics, and so came into line with the atomic views of mechanics and sociology.

Thus by the second half of the seventeenth century the major change-over had taken place in almost all fields, transforming the five relationships of reality from a medieval to a modern pattern. Cosmology had been fundamentally changed and man had stepped back, breaking almost all the containing medieval forms, and he now saw reality from a detached position. The new *object/cosmos* relationship was that of bodies moving in space. The new *object/object* relationship was that of corpuscular matter. The new *man/object* and *man/cosmos* relationships were the Cartesian dualism and the separation of the observer from his system of knowledge. And the new *man/man* relationship was that of an atomic and individualistic society.

This was the new pattern of the world when the major seventeenth century scientists made their great philosophical review of the universe.

CHAPTER VIII

THE CLASSICAL MODERN STATEMENTS:
GALILEO - DESCARTES - NEWTON

It was Galileo who achieved the union of the whole physical world into one continuum, and stated the final separation of the observer from physical reality. As a great maker of instruments he himself placed this filter or barrier between the observer and his system; and in his writings he was the first to define the new relationship, distinguishing clearly between the qualities that belong to matter and the qualities that belong to mind.

Discussing the nature of heat in *Il Saggiatore* (1623) Galileo points out that *motion* is a property of matter, but *heat* is only a human sensation:

> I have now only to fulfil my promise of declaring my opinions on the proposition that motion is the cause of heat, and to explain in what manner it appears to me that it may be true. But I must first make some remarks on what we call heat, since I strongly suspect that a notion prevails which is very remote from the truth; for it is believed that there is a true accident, affection, or quality, really inherent in the substance by which we feel ourselves heated. This much I have to say, that as soon as I form a conception of a material or corporeal substance, I simultaneously feel the

necessity of conceiving that it has its boundaries, and is of some shape or other; that, relative to others, it is great or small; that it is in this or that place, in this or that time; that it is in motion or at rest; that it touches, or does not touch, another body; that it is unique, rare, or common; nor can I, by any act of the imagination disjoin it from these qualities; but I do not find myself absolutely impelled to comprehend it as necessarily accompanied by such conditions as that it must be white or red, bitter or sweet, sonorous or silent, smelling sweetly or disagreeably; and if the senses had not pointed these qualities, it is probable that language and imagination alone could never have arrived at them. Therefore, I am inclined to think that these tastes, smells, colours, etc., with regard to the objects with which they appear to reside are nothing more than mere names, and exist only in the sensitive body in so much that when the living creature is removed all these qualities are carried off and annihilated; although we have imposed particular names upon them (different from those other and real accidents), and would fain persuade ourselves that they truly and in fact exist. But I do not believe that there exists anything in external bodies for exciting tastes, smells, and sounds, but size, shape, quantity, and motion, swift or slow; and if ears, tongues, and noses were removed, I am of opinion that shape, quantity and motion would remain, but there would be an end of smells, tastes and sounds, which abstractedly from the living creature, I take to be mere words [39].

---

[39] From *Il Saggiatore*. Quoted in *Galileo, his Life and Work*, by J. J. Fahie, 1903, p. 188.

204

This is a remarkable statement. Galileo sees the world of physical motion as so real, abstracted from such things as heat or colour, that he feels able to call one phenomenon physically true and the other merely a product of sensation. He feels he can clearly distinguish between an internal world of sensation and an external world of body and extension. Galileo's statement was perhaps more of a guess in the dark than a clear philosophical conclusion, but the fact that he made it shows that it was now possible to abstract motion in space from all other kinds of change; and that scientists were beginning to distinguish qualities that belong to the observer as a sensitive being, from qualities that belong to the physical world he is observing.

This distinction between *body* and *thought* was later deeply expounded by Descartes, but on the question of which attributes belong to body and which to thought, Descartes was less clear than Galileo, and he shows the difficulties that begin to arise if you consider the matter philosophically. Descartes first made a distinction between physical extension as one substance, and thinking mind as another.

> extension in length, breadth and depth, constitutes the nature of the Bodily Substance; and thought constitutes the nature of the Substance that Thinks. For everything else that one can attribute to body, presupposes extension, and is entirely dependent on that which is extended; similarly, all the properties that we

205

find in the thing that Thinks, are only different ways of thinking [40].

On this basis he then discusses the difference between the qualities of body and the qualities of sensation. He extracts 'extension' as the only quality necessary to the existence of body:

> we should know that the Nature of Matter or of Body, taken as a whole, does not consist in its being something hard, or heavy, or coloured, or that touches our senses in any other way; but only in that it is a Substance Extended in length, breadth and depth. As regards Hardness, we only know of it by touch, in that the particles of hard bodies resist the movement of our hands when they meet with them: But if on every occasion that we placed our hands anywhere, the bodies that are in that place withdrew as fast as our hands approached it is certain that we would not feel any hardness; yet nevertheless we would have no reason to believe that the bodies that withdrew in this way were to lose thereby their quality of being bodies. From which it follows that their nature does not consist in the hardness we sometimes feel in them; nor in the weight, heat, and other qualities of this type: For if we examine any body whatsoever, we can imagine it to have none of these qualities, but we nevertheless recognise clearly and distinctly that it will have everything that makes it a body, as long as it has extension in length, width and depth. From which it

---

[40] René Descartes: *Les Principes de la Philosophie*, Part I. Paragraph 53.

follows also that in order to Be, it has no need whatsoever of the other qualities, and that its nature consists only in its being a substance which is extended.

Descartes has left the problem in an unsatisfactory
state because he has not properly defined the 'unneces-
sary' qualities of matter. The problem was tackled once
again by Locke, who distinguished between *primary* qualities of a body such as size, and *secondary* qualities such
as colour or heat. But this only confuses the issue by
suggesting different degrees of reality in the physical
world itself. The problem of sensations troubled philosophers and Galileo's statement remained the clearest
way of saying what everybody was really assuming.

In practice what scientists from the seventeenth century onwards did was to place *instruments* of measurement (either physical or metaphorical) between the
objects they were observing and themselves: the telescope, the thermometer, the weighing scale, the quantitative analysis. And with this intermediate barrier or
sieve standing between the observer and his reality, the
question of sensations was avoided, and all the qualities
of heat and cold, or other cosmic opposites, which had
played such an important part in medieval thought, were
simply eliminated. These instruments reduced and reinterpreted all the information into quantitative terms.
Newton's prism was an instrument of this kind — reducing colour to numerical analysis. The telescope and the
microscope extended the field of human vision in both

directions, made man increasingly aware of relative size, and helped to discredit human proportions as the norm for cosmic magnitudes.

Superficially instruments merely re-interpret information in quantitative terms. However, these intermediary instruments are an important feature of the scientific method. They remove the scientist himself from the scene. In the Middle Ages knowledge was the immediate formulation of direct experience. But henceforth the scientist works away from the material he is studying. His knowledge is built up, as it were in a different room, into which numerical information about the outside world is handed in through the intermediary of the scientific instrument. The scientist is himself blind, and uses instruments instead of eyes to make his observations for him.

This has a certain philosophical importance. It confirms the separation of the observer from his knowledge. But it also means that knowledge will *not* consist henceforth of *experience* — such as emotions, instincts, religious insight, or sensations. Modern knowledge will be of quite a different kind.

Medieval thought originated from man's *experience*. Modern thought originates from man's *experiment*. In the 16th century there was no basic difference in meaning between these two words. It was said that a man was an *experimented* man, meaning an experienced man. But in the 17th century the two words part company, and diverge into their Cartesian compartments: the human and

208

the scientific. Only in French, a language of very small vocabulary, does the phrase *faire une expérience* still mean to make an experiment.

The instruments themselves, standing half way between the observer and his system, are sometimes classed as belonging to the observer, and sometimes as belonging to the physical system which he is observing. In recent years, with quantum mechanics and relativity, their status has taken on a new importance. It has been found in microscopic observation that the use of light or nuclear particles for observing affects the observed system, at the moment that it is being observed.

Eddington's net explains this: that we will find the fish in the sea to be according to the sized net we use to catch them with. The net is part of the physical world, but it is also part of the observer, and determines, like his eyes and ears, what knowledge he will receive.

This whole question is only one example of the more general principle I have been formulating: that by determining what status the observer has, man alters the kind of experiences he will receive, and the type of knowledge that he acquires. His scientific instruments are a way of defining who the observer is. The use of instruments from the 17th century onwards has determined that man's knowledge of the world, like his experience of his own status, will be *objective*.

*   *   *

It was Descartes who made the most complete and important philosophical statement about the separation between the individual observer and the physical world, with his famous dualism. This dualism, as we have been seeing, was achieved over several centuries, and Descartes' statement is only the final formulation of it. As a philosopher he did not think of the dualism in a historical context, nor as something peculiar to his day. He thought of it in absolute terms, true to all times and to all men. His is a classical example of a philosophy that is the product and expression of its age, yet is formulated in general terms that would apply equally to all ages, and are generally thought to do so.

Descartes' whole method of argument is interesting because it contains a self-conscious formulation of the scientific method, and shows at the same time the particular mentality and psychological approach of the scientist.

Descartes has described for us how he decided to question everything, and then build up gradually a new system of philosophy based only on his own clear ideas, and on what he himself could fully comprehend. The philosophy that he was questioning was the old medieval philosophy, the accumulated work of many thinkers — in his opinion a composite affair:

> One of the first thoughts I had was that I advised myself to consider that there is often not so much perfection in works composed from various pieces,

and made by the hand of several masters, as in those on which only one man has worked [41].

Therefore the individual — 'I' myself — is to be the thinking unit. Descartes next rejects his own childhood thoughts because they are confused and unclear:

> And in this way I also thought that as we were children before being men, and we were necessarily governed for a long time by our appetites and our tutors, which were sometimes opposed to each other, and neither of which perhaps always gave us the best advice, it is almost impossible that our judgments should be as pure nor as solid as they would be if we had had the use of our reason from the moment of our birth, and had only been led by her (p. 13).

This is a general rejection of the past. Descartes next proceeded to a methodical doubting of everything, in fact to a *method* of doubt, into which he says he had to force himself. Through this he laid down four precepts on which he would try to construct his knowledge. The first precept was to accept only those ideas which he — 'I' — can fully and clearly comprehend:

> The first was not to receive anything as true which I did not clearly recognise as such: that is to say to avoid carefully precipitation and prejudice, and not

---

[41] P. 12.   This and the following quotations are taken from Descartes: *Discours de la Méthode.*   Manchester University Press. 1941.   My translation.

to receive anything in my judgment other than that which appeared so clearly and so distinctly to my spirit, that I had no occasion to doubt it (p. 18).

His second precept was to analyse and divide everything down to its smallest necessary parts:

> The second, was to divide each of the problems that I examined, in as many parts as were possible, and necessary for their best solution (p. 18).

This is the modern analytical method. Elsewhere Descartes has described the infinite or indefinite divisibility of quantity:

> as one could never imagine dividing a body into such small parts, that each one of these parts could not be divided into even smaller ones, we will believe that quantity can be divided into an indefinite number of parts [42].

Descartes also states elsewhere that time is divisible in this way, like quantity. He says that in mechanics the present does not depend upon the past as a formal unity (the medieval idea). Everything can in fact be analysed and understood in the present, without recourse to this formal and organic unity:

> The present time does not depend on that which has immediately preceded it; that is why there is the need

---

[42] *Les Principes de la Philosophie.* Part I. Para. 26.

of no less a cause for conserving a thing, than for producing it for the first time [43].

In his own algebraic geometry Descartes could treat time as infinitely divisible and measurable, like a spatial coordinate.

To return to his method, his third precept follows directly from the second: to build up composite knowledge, or complexes, out of smaller or more simple units:

> The third, was to order my ideas, by starting with the objects that are simpler and easier to understand, and rise slowly, as though by degrees, until I understood the most composite ones, even assuming such order among things that do not naturally precede each other in this way (p. 19).

This is the second step of analysis: to build up a synthetic structure from the units which the analysis has reached. This reveals a common scientific assumption — though not a happy one in biology — that a large structure is composed of simpler units, and of the external relationship between these units. In other words, that the whole is never more than the parts — as it was in the medieval system of thought.

The fourth precept lays down Descartes' aim at an overall completeness and comprehensiveness in his knowledge:

---

[43] *Axioms.*

And the last was, to make everywhere such complete analyses, and such general reviews that I would be assured of not omitting anything (p. 19).

With these four precepts in mind Descartes then set out to doubt everything, and review everything afresh. In this he acted as an *observer* looking at the world detachedly, rather than as an *actor* involved in the human drama. He specifically says that this is how he spent his time:

> And for the following nine years, I did nothing more than wander here and there over the globe, trying to be a spectator rather than an actor in all the comedies that are played there (p. 28).

In his search for truth, and by his method of doubting, he reached his famous conclusion:

> But immediately after, I was careful to note that while I was trying to think in this way that everything was false, it was necessary for I myself who was thinking this, to be something; and remarking that this truth, *I think, therefore I am*, was so firm and so certain[...] I judged that I could accept it without scruples as the first principle of the philosophy I was seeking (p. 31). [...] I recognised from this that I was a substance whose essence or whose nature it is to think, and who, to exist, does not require any place nor depend on anything material: so that this 'I', that is to say the soul, by which I am what I am, is entirely distinct from body (p. 32).

Descartes then proceeds, in a curious medieval way, to deduce from his own clear thoughts about perfection, that there must be a God, and from this proceeds downward again, via God, to a knowledge of the existence of a physical world of extension. The result of this was to produce a dualism between thought and matter, as two distinct worlds or substances:

> We can therefore have two clear or distinct ideas, or notions, one of a created substance that thinks, and the other of an extended substance [44].

So Descartes, like Galileo before him, saw all activity in the physical world as motion of place, or extension, and believed that the true understanding of physical activity is in these terms, and not in terms of heat or colour or hardness. He says of the philosopher, that he will do well

> Above all if he considers that he knows well[...] what is the size of the body that he is observing, or the shape or the movement, at any rate that movement which is made from one place to another (because philosophers pretending that there are other movements than this one, have not properly understood its true nature), or the placing of the parts, or the duration or the number of them, and those properties that are to be perceived clearly in all bodies [45].

---

[44] *Les Principes de la Philosophie.* Part I. Para. 54.
[45] *Les Principes de la Philosophie.* Part I. Para. 69.

These quotations show that Descartes' philosophy lies at the heart of the scientific method. The general difference between medieval and Cartesian thought is clear from the fact that the medieval thinker stood *inside* his system of thought, and the Cartesian thinker stands detachedly and self-consciously apart. It is impossible therefore for the Cartesian mind to understand the subjective and internal world of the Middle Ages — at any rate as something externally true, and not merely in his own mind. By defining himself Descartes has tacitly defined his knowledge.

The importance of the Cartesian dualism is *not* that it distinguishes between body and soul; this distinction had always existed in the Middle Ages, and is one of the principal doctrines of Christian thought. The importance of the Cartesian dualism is that is distinguishes and separates the *observer*, the thinking 'I', from the *objects he is observing*. This is something that the Middle Ages never did.

Descartes, in his dualism, was not talking about *soul* as a *thing*, he is talking about the thinking 'I'; though he himself reverted to medieval terminology and confused his own definitions. The Cartesian thinking 'I' applies only to myself, because 'I' am the only thing that thinks. Descartes in his method was not referring to man in general, as the Middle Ages did when they spoke of body and soul — he is referring only to the individual 'I'. He is distinguishing between I who think, and the physical world of extension which I think about. It was only as a

216

result of extreme *self*-consciousness that Descartes was able to define the thinking 'I' as something separate from extension.

Therefore in the Cartesian dualism *other* people are merely objects of the physical world who can be studied and looked at. Descartes' theory implies a distinction between 'I' who think and 'You' who are merely an object. Descartes himself, however, used general terms like 'thought' and 'soul', so that he was never fully aware of this difference between 'I' and 'You'. It was because Descartes himself was not clear on this point that he made several mistakes in the subsequent development of his dualism.

The Cartesian dualism is the crowning achievement of individual objectivity. It states the fundamental principles of the classical scientific method: that the scientist or observer is not included in the system he is observing; that his system of knowledge is related to the thinking individual 'I'; and that this thinking 'I' has a position in space, yet is himself paradoxically separate from it.

Dualisms are not popular, because they suggest a separation which the very statement of their existence seems to deny. By declaring a dualism you imply that there is a connection between both parts. So having created his dualism (which lies at the heart of science), Descartes tried his best to resolve it. He did this by falling into medieval terminology, and confused his own concepts. Firstly, he defined his dualism in traditional philosophical terms, as a difference between Thought and Extension, or rather a thinking *substance* and an extended *substance*. By this means he hid from himself the difference between 'I' and 'You'. So he believed that he had discovered two *substances,* or in other words two 'objects'. He then presented himself with the problem: how are these two substances related? Since the brain, he said (jumping even further towards viewing thought as a physical object) — since the brain is in the head, the mind must be connected to the body somewhere in the brain, since we know that the mind has an effect on the body. Descartes finally decided on the pineal gland as the point in the brain where the mind and the body meet.

In this sequence of thought he lost the whole of his dualism, by formulating the thinking 'I' into the general concept of *mind,* and thence viewing mind as an object, and finally giving it a position in space. His mistake was to try to solve the problem, as it were, on another animal, so that, looking at the brain of the other animal, he assumed that animal to have thought as well as body. He slipped from the subjective thinking 'I' to the objective thinking 'You' and 'He', without noticing that he was sliding away from his first definition, and so circumvented his own original definition of the thinking 'I' as something separate from the world of extension.

The problem of the Cartesian dualism has remained; and many philosophers since Descartes have tried to resolve it. The problem is important because of its direct application to the scientific method, and its implied or

218

hidden criticism of that method. Philosophers one after another have had recourse to Descartes' own way of hiding and covering up the dualism by treating the thinking 'I' under the general term of *mind* — and then transferring it silently from a *subjective* concept to an external and analysable *object*. Locke, Berkeley and Hume were all faced with the Cartesian dualism. Locke did the same as Descartes: he reduced the 'I' to the general concept of Mind, and then treated it as an object. Berkeley did the reverse, and transferred the whole of the physical world into mind, by saying that everything is thought.

> Note: Lest it should be felt that my interpretation of the history of thought is too Berkeleyan in its conception and approach — since I seem to claim that all reality is relative to a thinker — let me say on my own account that there is one experience (out of many) which I have always felt (even in my most introspective moods) to demonstrate the continued existence of a world separate from my own thought. Sometimes when I return home and open the door of my room, I find the electric light on and the whole room in general disorder. And with a shock of surprise I remember that this is how I had left it earlier on, when I had been called away in a hurry — so the continued existence of the room in this state seems to *contradict* my own thoughts and expectations. Anybody who has had the same experience will know what I mean.

* * *

In the present twentieth century, scientists and philosophers are still trying to cover and smudge over the Cartesian dualism, and many believe that it has been resolved. A number of false solutions are offered. Here are three of them:

False solutions: 1) In quantum mechanics it has been found that the observer affects the system he is observing, and in relativity his presence and position in space are important; and it is sometimes argued that he now therefore belongs to the system he is observing, and that the dualism has been resolved. But it is not the thinking 'I', it is only the *instruments* he uses which affect the system in quantum mechanics, and it is not the 'I', only the position of his *body* which is relevant in astronomy. Therefore this does not solve the dualism. It makes no difference to the Cartesian dualism whether the world of extension is something *absolutely* true independent of any observer, or whether it only exists in relation to an observer, as modern science prefers.

2) Another way of trying to overcome the Cartesian dualism is to postulate two observers, so that they appear to include each other in their systems of thought, even though they do not include themselves directly. But in this case the *other* observer is merely, of course, a physical object, or at best an intermediary instrument, and not an 'I' at all.

3) Another attempt is often made to eliminate the dualism of mind and matter through the intermediate

and difficult ground of *sensations*. This repeats Descartes' confusion between *my* thought and *other* people's sensations. It was a medieval tenet that there is nothing in the mind which has not first come from the senses; and this is roughly speaking the mechanical modern view. Therefore all thought can be reduced to sensations, and all sensations are, as Hobbes said, merely the product of the motion of bodies, such as light on the eye and softness on the skin. Sensations are therefore purely mechanical events. It is on this theory that complicated machines constructed today are said to 'think', and to have a 'memory'. But any such opinion jumps invisibly from one side to the other of the dualism, on the word 'sensation': sensation is made to cover not only what 'I' feel and think, but the electrical impulses or chemistry that I observe in somebody *else*'s brain and nervous system. This is Descartes' own confusion.

If we are to make any comparison between thought and the brain, several problems have to be faced. The most important one is: how does the *organisation* of one tally with the *organisation* of the other? For example an automatic assumption underlying 'thinking' machines is the assumption that thoughts have *quantity*. In what sense do they have quantity?

Problems: 1) I may think of the thousandth part of an electron, or of fifty-five oranges, but these thoughts have nothing to do with the thousandth part of an electron, or of fifty-five oranges as they exist in space, with a measurable dimension and extension. Therefore there is no direct correlation here between thought and objects.

2)   As I have tried to show, systems of thought change their organisation from one person to another and from one age to another, but this organisation has patently nothing to do with *quantity* in a spatial or extended sense — it is a matter of mental and *qualitative* analysis: and *mental* analysis is not the same thing as division and analysis in *quantity*.

3)   Given the two previous problems: does *number* ever mean the same thing on either side of the Cartesian dualism?

4)   I find it hard to believe that extended nature is about number. If one peach is lying on the ground and another peach falls, what there is, is one peach and another peach. It is difficult to believe that there are two peaches; and that the first peach has become part of two peaches without there being any change in it. This argument would even apply to the patterns on a pine cone, which are always regular. There is no indication that nature has anything to do with number in any cumulative sense. Number is what we decide to relate.

5)   What about number on the other side of the Cartesian dualism? We have seen already that the 'idea of number' has nothing to do with number itself (see problem 1). Viewed detachedly, do *ideas themselves* have number? If we speak we mouth a certain *number* of words. But words are already in the external or extended world. Whether ideas themselves have number is

not at all clear. Ideas are not the same as the words that are used to express them, as anybody will know who has tried to write. I often have quite a clear idea, and it is only with the greatest effort, by trial and error, that I can manage to express it in words.

6) Can one then have two ideas about the same thing? — this would introduce number into thought. But it is not clear that I myself can have two different views on one particular topic: this would merely involve the kind of organisation we have observed with the peaches: to see number here would be our arbitrary decision. The presence of number might be found in 'two different ideas about reality': because these would clearly be two ideas about one thing, not just 'contradictory' views — nor would the two ideas be reducible to one. But the organisation here is probably the same as that of the peaches.

Therefore, discarding number for the time being as a useful intermediary between the two sides of the Cartesian dualism, can *the organisation of ideas* be transferred in any way to *the organisation of matter?*

Attempts are regularly made to discover patterns in thought. This is perhaps the only way that thought can be known to have any organisation at all. Let me take three examples of such patterns: (i) The most obvious kind of pattern is any system of reality itself. Let us take medieval cosmology as an example of this. (ii) A second type of organisation is that of psychology, which rearranges thoughts into a pattern of its own. Freud, for example, talked of the *sub*-conscious; Jung avoided any crude analogy with space and talked of the *un*conscious. But both these and other depth psychologists have constructed systems of organisation. (iii) A third example is the system I have myself constructed here in a Theory of Knowledge (see p. 95).

These three are in a sense already deceptive intermediaries, which we may try to transfer into a machine or physical system.

(i) The medieval system is not included in the modern spatial one for the reasons that I have expounded in this work. Therefore the transference from medieval thought to any mechanical or spatial system cannot be made.

(ii) An attempt to equate the organisation of psychology with the organisation of physics, would be to equate the spatial patterns of psychology with the space of physics, when these clearly have nothing to do with each other. The two patterns are based on a different 'space' or order. You cannot therefore transfer organisation from thought to space in this way.

(iii) If, taking my own theory of knowledge as the pattern, you assume a basically Berkeleyan view, and try to relate *space* and *thought* through the mind, you cannot do so since space is only one particular unit of thought, belonging to the individual observer with a certain mental objec-

224

tivity. Therefore to include mind in space would be to include a greater inside a lesser — which our present method of thinking at any rate would not know how to do.

Conversely, any attempt to correlate a shifting system of relationships such as I have expounded, into a fixed cellular pattern, would probably be to reduce it to a fixed set of units. Therefore there would be no such thing as a system of relationships, but only a limited though complex number of set units. Therefore either you cannot transfer knowledge to cells, or alternatively my whole theory must be incorrect. And if my pattern does not exist, you cannot then transfer it.

The only way to correlate mind and body, or thought and extension, would be for a purpose, and *according* to the purpose that we have in mind. For medical reasons we wish to know what part of the brain works on what system — that purpose justifies and corroborates any correlation. Any purpose we may have is a sufficient link, whereas no detached view of the problem seems to provide a sufficient link. Here may lie the answer. Probably the Cartesian dualism should be expanded into something more interesting, rather than crushed back into monism.

*　*　*

Newton's major philosophical thought lies in his *Principia* (1687) where he expounds his theory of gravitation and his system of mechanics. His book became the foundation stone of modern classical physics and the philosophical core of the objective scientific method.

Newton operates from both directions — *deductively* by mathematical principles and pure logic, and *inductively* by generalisation from nature. At the point where these two methods coincide he constructs his theory of gravitation. In other words, he shows mathematically that his system is only one logical thing; and then by induction he raises the phenomena of nature and simplifies their causes until they are seen to coincide with this one simple phenomenon, the force of gravity. He totally identifies mathematical logic with the phenomena of nature. Numbers will explain everything in nature; the rest is illusion and fantasy.

He explains his method of induction in his four *Rules of Reasoning in Philosophy*, in Book III of the *Principia*. (By 'philosophy' he means 'natural philosophy', the seventeenth century term for 'science').

> *Rule i.* We are to admit no more causes of natural things than such as are both true and sufficient to explain their appearance.
>
> *Rule ii.* Therefore to the same natural effects we must, as far as possible, assign the same causes.

This is really Occam's razor: don't multiply terms unnecessarily.

226

Rule iii. The qualities of bodies, which admit neither intensification nor remission of degrees, and which are found to belong to all bodies within the reach of our experiments, are to be esteemed the universal qualities of all bodies whatsoever.

Rule iv. In experimental philosophy we are to look upon propositions inferred by general induction from phenomena as accurately or very nearly true, notwithstanding any contrary hypothesis that may be imagined, till such time as other phenomena occur, by which they may either be made more accurate, or liable to exceptions.

In other words, keep the system open to absorb more and more information until all reality has been brought in and incorporated into the system. Newton thus raises us in generality towards one absolute cause or system for all phenomena.

In the mathematical part he proceeds by a similar set of principles, which he tacitly follows, though without stating them. I summarise his views as follows:

1. His destructive analysis and his constructive building follow identical paths, as who should take a mechanism to pieces and put it together again.
2. For Newton the whole is identical with its parts. His system is nothing more than the bricks that are contained in it.
3. He analyses a phenomenon down indefinitely

from the outside until he reaches a mere infinitesimal *point* (the point of gravity). All the rest is space or external relationship. Therefore his system consists only of the analysed and external relationship between ultimately irreducible points. 4. There is no human *experience* involved in his observation of nature other than the *motion* of parts in space.

Newton is not concerned with the senses, nor with anything subjective, because for him the observer is so detached that his presence has to all appearances been eliminated in *objectivity*, as though he were a God. Newton is however relying on *one* experience: the motions of body in space. But these motions can be measured by instruments and do not even require the sensations or presence of an observer. Thus virtually no human experiences are used or required in order to discover the truths of nature. There is a minimum of interference by the observer and a minimum of human experience involved.

Newton's elimination of internal qualities in nature, and his withdrawal of the observer, therefore reach a limit at three vital points:

1. Newton can analyse natural forces (i.e. gravity) down to a *point*, but not beyond; that point or centre of gravity still exists, and the full attractive force issues from it. The force is not analysed *beyond* this point and

eliminated altogether. This is very important. It reveals that complete analysis from the outside, by reducing something to its parts, is illusory; it can never completely understand the phenomena nor actually reduce the forces of the whole, it can only drive them back or down to a point.

In other words, analysis from the outside (which is the method of objective science) assumes that we are working upon something which has internal qualities (otherwise it would not be analysis from the outside), rather as bouncing a ball against a wall presupposes the existence of the wall. Analysis from the outside diminishes the size of the units of nature, and unmixes the forces; but it never eliminates the internal qualities against which the external analysis is battling. It is rather like a process of entering room after room, and watching the life-force withdrawing into yet another inner room, even smaller and smaller or further away. This is perhaps why Leibnitz accused Newton of having postulated in gravity an occult force in nature.

2. The fact that Newton is analysing *motion of bodies in space* also shows that he *is* in fact using one human experience to collect his information. He cannot operate if he has no contact with nature at all. But Newton was convinced that motion in space is an absolute external reality outside himself and independent of himself, and he did not realise that it was precisely here where he was resting his system on a subjective experience.

Therefore it seems from Newton's work that the objective method relies on at least one *subjective* piece of information, however minimal, and however disguised it may be as an 'objective phenomenon'.

3. Newton personally managed to render himself so objective that he assumed he was *nowhere*, and space and God were *everywhere*. This was the relation he managed to convince himself of, as between the two sides of the Cartesian dualism. It was the absence of Newton and the presence of bodies in space. And his theory of mechanics was therefore considered the epitome and triumph of *absolutely objective* science; where the whole system of the world could be understood by *one* person. And here is Newton's third subjective pivot: that he needs one observer to have a system of reality at all. It is his third tacit subjective assumption, because a system that could for example, only be understood by three people conjointly would be different in kind from a single-minded system — and therefore neither one nor the other type of system is totally objective nor independent of an observer.

Thus, as we learn in Newton's work, the imperceptible limits of objectivity are three-fold: You must have at least *one* man who can comprehend the whole of the mechanics; at least *one* phenomenon or experience has to be used (in this case the motion of bodies in space); and the internal forces of nature can be analysed down to *one* point (such as the centre of gravity), but no further, since this point with its internal qualities cannot be eliminated altogether. One man; one experience; one object.

That was as far as absolute objective detachment could reach in withdrawing from subjectivity. It could not totally eliminate these three single subjective points, but on the contrary rested its whole superstructure on them.

Now let us, in practice, watch Newton at his apparently objective analytical method, as he reduces the phenomena of the world's mechanics down to these three subjective pivots:

Newton's theory of gravitation is staggeringly simple, and his way of demonstrating it shows his analytical technique in all its clarity and beauty. We can see here how his method of analysis is the same as his method of composition (this is true for any system built up externally out of its parts).

He first explains that a body (say the earth) moves naturally in a straight line, unless it is deflected by some other force (say the attractive force of the sun). He shows that if the earth is moving in a straight line from A to B, and is simultaneously deflected by a force from

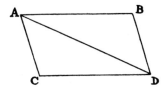

the sun pulling it from A to C; it will, if both forces are acting together, be pulled across the parallelogram of forces from A to D. He then shows that the earth is deflected in this way by the sun, through an infinite

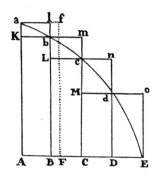

number of minute parallelograms of force, to move round the sun in a curve. The earth moving naturally from *a* to *f*, will be deflected by the attractive force of the Sun at *A* to move in a curve *abcdE*. Therefore he has analysed a curved motion round the sun into two single straight line forces; and he has simultaneously shown that the two straight line forces operating together will produce a curved motion. His analysis and his methods of composition are identical and simultaneous. Newton always keeps strictly to a monistic system in all his mechanics. For him every complex activity can be broken down to its simple parts. He never envisages an activity which is in itself a complex motion.

He then shows us how to calculate elliptical, parabolic and hyperbolic motions round an attractive point — and in this way incorporates Kepler's laws of planetary motion into his theory. He shows that the attractive force of gravity from the sun will fully explain the elliptical orbits of the planets, and therefore no other motive

232

force could be causing them to move round the Sun in this way.

He then turns to the attractive force operating on falling bodies, and studies straight-line ascent and descent of bodies — and thus incorporates Galileo's law of falling bodies into his theory. He is gradually incorporating one natural phenomen after another into his system.

He then combines the curved motion of a body round a centripetal point (Kepler's planetary laws) with straight up and down motion (Galileo's law of falling bodies), into one mechanical system; and thus unites all terrestrial and heavenly motions under one single law of gravitation.

Having completed his study of a single body in motion, he analyses two or more bodies which are mutually attracting each other. He shows that the common centre of gravity between several bodies will itself operate like a single and simple body. So mechanically speaking a single tiny body, or a large mass, or a collection of separate bodies with a common centre of gravity, will all act in the same way. All matter is made up of mere groupings of indefinitely small particles. Newton can therefore show that the same mechanical laws apply to the smallest particle, or to any group of particles forming a large body, or to any group of separate large bodies like the stars or planets that act upon each other at a distance. The simplicity of it is staggering. By this little step of referring everything to a 'common centre of gravity' he builds a mechanical system which can range from the smallest particles to the largest cosmic structures.

By uniting his theory of particles with his theory of planets (the internal with the external), he explains that the whole action of a system will always be an attraction inwards towards the single particle that lies at the centre of gravity:

> For the attraction of every particle is inversely as the square of its distance from the centre of the attracting sphere, (Prop. 74), and is therefore the same as if that whole attracting force issued from one single corpuscle placed in the centre of this sphere (Book I. Theorem 35).

By reducing all order to this one single corpuscle at the centre, he has completed his analysis and has built his theory of gravitation — but beyond this ultimate central point he cannot go.

He imagines particles as very closely packed in solids, more diffuse in liquids, more separated still in vapours, and in the heavens so diffuse and rarely spaced that they do not even interfere with the movement of the planets. His table of structures from solids, to liquids, to vapour, to light consists only in a greater or lesser packing of particles.

Newton's world, so far as the mechanics are concerned, is therefore made up of innumerable identical particles, which are grouped together to form larger and larger bodies. In other words, he has given us a system with no structure, only a ladder of magnitude and arrangement of parts; and no qualities in any particle or group of particles that are not held by all particles and groups alike.

Newton has shown that the whole gravitational force can be calculated as issuing from the central point of gravity of any body or group or system. Therefore there is no difference between the inside and the outside of a body, nor between one body and a group of bodies, so far as the mechanics are concerned. He has apparently made the complete external breakdown, the complete analysis of matter. In Newtonian mechanics there is no difference between *inside* and *outside,* everything can be analysed down to its indefinitely small parts — and this was to become an axiom of modern classical physics.

He has not suggested any upper or lower limit of magnitude where this divisibility ceases. It is a system where, at first sight, the internal and the external appear to have merged. But in fact he has merely analysed the internal world further and further in, until he has reduced it to *one point,* the point at the centre of gravity. And this is a mighty powerful irreducible point. His is an *everywhere/nowhere* system, where the sum of the parts equal the whole, where all the universe operates by *one* force, and this force has been analysed down to the *one* point at the centre of gravity; and the whole structure of the universe consists of external relationships between these points, or centres of gravity.

Therefore the three great theorists of modern objectiv-

ity — Galileo, Descartes and Newton — while each
defining 'objectivity' in his own way, have revealed the
three subjective pivots on which scientific objectivity
actually rests. Galileo has shown that knowledge needs
at least *one observation* or experience — in his case the
sight of a moving body. Descartes has shown that it
needs *one subjective observer* who is doing the thinking or
knowing. And Newton has shown that all mechanical
activity can be reduced and analysed down to *one force,*
but not beyond. And beyond a single observer, a single
experience and a single force, objective analysis cannot go.

CHAPTER IX

THE LIMITS OF INDIVIDUAL OBJECTIVITY

Having traced the history of classical modern objectivity to its highest point, we can now follow its development and decline.

I first want to make clear what we are studying. From the Middle Ages to present times our information about the natural world has increased steadily. No genuine observation made by them has been rejected by us. But the system of *interpreting* the observations has altered to such an extent that one system of thought has been totally rejected in favour of another. We are studying here not the increase of knowledge, but this shift between systems of thought.

The knowledge that man has acquired will doubtless increase further, but our system of understanding and interpreting — what I have called our cosmology, system of reality, or ethos — will undoubtedly shift once again; and the knowledge that man has accumulated will be reinterpreted into a new system.

So let us study the units of our present objective system, and note how they are already beginning to alter and move into something else. My theory of knowledge as shifting relationships — assuming it to be correct — allows considerable flexibility. The number of relationships involved, and their type, is obviously arbitrary. I usually refer to five basic relationships, but in my definition of *Principle 4* on page 96 I have treated them as only three. And I am not even pretending that I have identified the most important five. What is important is not the number of relationships, nor their kind, nor any labels, but the fact that they are so interwoven that they shift and change together. This means that a basic change made in the relation between objects, will reveal a new type of relationship in existence between people; and conversely, the discovery of a new relationship between people will open the way for a whole range of discoveries about nature. And if man's relation to the world is altered or explained further by some new type of consciousness, or fundamental experience, this should widen and enrich all the other relationships.

But how can we even pretend to guess the future? Historians face a curious unscientific phenomenon: The events of history follow each other in sequence — or at least I think they do. Looking back we can understand the link of one event with another: but looking forward it is impossible to predict safely even one step ahead. Facile predictions like those of Marx and other economists who take the *present* state of affairs and extend it forwards into the future like a projected image, are valueless.

Historians know that they cannot predict, and yet they also know with equal clarity that they can understand the sequence of events. This would be puzzling to a physicist for whom *prediction* and *understanding* are synonymous.

One way to illustrate this puzzle is perhaps as follows: If you take a pencil and draw over paper a single meandering line, you leave a pattern behind you — perhaps the drawing of a profile or face. Every part of the pattern can be related to every other part, but you cannot by this means foretell which way the pencil is going to move next, nor what pattern is about to emerge. There is a *change* although there is a *constant sequence*. Physics, and most of the sciences generally, are looking for a sequence without change, where the same pattern repeats itself again and again, and can be foreknown.

Their aim is how to find a *constant* within the flux of change. So at one extreme the sciences will admit no real change; at the other extreme the arts admit no absolute constant.

In practice the physicist seeks constant *material;* and the biologist and sociologist tend to seek constant *patterns* or forms. I have sought a constant *relationship* between all of these, trying to steer a middle course by seeing in my five interlinking relationships a kind of constant. But as a proper historian I do not pretend to know in what way any pencil will move next, except the pencil that I am manipulating myself.

* * *

However, to dash my own theory aside, let us hazard a

guess. In order to break through the boundaries of present knowledge we must first discover its limits. Once you can detect a limit you have surpassed it. And we can then move through to something else. So let us start by outlining the professed limits of modern reality, which are essentially the limits of modern classical science.

As Descartes has shown, our modern experience of reality is divided into two separate compartments: *objective experience* and *subjective experience*. The aim of objective science is to keep these two as separate as possible — even to the point of schizophrenia — in order to maintain the objective compartment pure. Newton has further shown that the aim of classical scientific thought is to unify all knowledge under one mind, one instrument, and one force or cause. Indeed we might almost define present-day reality by saying that *modern scientific reality can be fully comprehended by any one person, and fully communicated to any other person.* What are the implications of this?

Modern knowledge of reality is based on a monistic system, in the sense that one person can follow through all its corridors, and understand every branch of it, and all its links. There is no knowledge today which needs *two* or more thinkers to be undertood, nor which is based on multi-people thought.

Modern knowledge can also be fully communicated from any one person to any other person, because it relies on only the very simplest and most universal human experiences which we all share: like common sense, or the ability to count, see, measure and think logically. Modern reality is therefore both single-minded and simple-minded.

Thinkers have achieved this very simple basis both by withdrawing all possible extraneous and 'subjective' material, and by collecting all knowledge together into one consistent system. This has proved very useful for building systems of *prediction* (which is fundamentally what modern science is all about). But it is limiting. There is something unsatisfactory about a knowledge of reality which is unable to use either more complex or more important experiences. Our own life tells us that reality includes *every* experience.

There is also something limited in a reality which depends only on the single mind. But nobody has known how to break down this boundary successfully, nor demonstrate conclusively that there is such a thing as multi-mind thinking. The communication of knowledge from one person to another suggests that there may be such a thing as shared experience, but we do not know at all clearly what this communication between people involves. It is a problem on the 'I' side of the Cartesian dualism. We cannot simply explain human communication as a mechanical 'passing of information' similar to any other physical or mechanical activity. We should perhaps invert the problem, and try to discover what *understanding*, *sympathy* and *communication* between 'subjective' people could possibly mean. The answer to this

241

might tell us a lot about the nature of our present 'objective' knowledge.

Modern knowledge is also fully comprehensible in another sense: The units of reality do not contain any 'uncontrolled' or 'unanalysed' entities. A phenomenon is always analysed down to as many simple parts as possible, and our knowledge consists only of the resulting relationship between the parts. Our definition of a body is entirely in terms of its external relationship to other bodies: that it moves faster or slower than another, that it is attracted to another, and so on. Therefore modern knowledge consists of fully comprehensible units (even a statement about internal disorder rests on an assumption about order) — and is in this way limited to *controlled* knowledge and controlled experience. It excludes the vast area of uncontrolled knowledge and experience, and that of variable information.

The fact that knowledge is at present both single-minded and universally communicable tallies with the fact that our thinker today is *individual/everybody,* and our reality is *unique/universal.* Every event in science is unique (the medieval idea of universal realism is really finished) as regards time and space. But all material is understood in universal terms. When a body is analysed today it is always reduced to its *universal* basic particles. Even a living being is analysed in structure down to universal chemical particles which have no unique qualities to them other than those of being in a particular place and time.

242

This excludes several other types of event: When a dancer dances she does what she will never do again. But modern thought is incapable of understanding the event because it is unique. If she were to repeat the same dance, it would be a repetition of a unique event, and modern knowledge would still know nothing about it. It can accept only the 'always-everywhere' event. In other words, it does not yet accept experiences which only a limited number of people have; nor material which is not universal; nor an event which is unique or rare.

This indicates that the bounds of modern physical reality will be broken the moment you can either (i) find a group-thinker or other thinker; (ii) discover how to accept *non*-universal events in a body of science which is concerned mainly with prediction; or (iii) learn how to incorporate experiences and phenomena that are not 'fully comprehensible' nor amenable to analysis of the modern kind.

Finally it is important to note that modern knowledge, like art, is a projection. I have mentioned this before. The scientist working in his laboratory or office is projecting his problems onto pieces of paper. His reality is not direct, as an emotional experience would be. It is constructed, projected like art onto a limited surface or into limited equations, or like literature into written words, and understood there. Not nearly enough attention has been payed to this fact of projection. It suggests that there is another kind of knowledge available — direct experience — which today is hardly being used at all;

this would be *experiencing* and *receiving* knowledge. Modern projected knowledge is the reverse: it is an *expression* of man, like art: the giving out of a pattern. In this sense modern reality is an expression by ourselves rather than an impression received or experienced.

This projecting capacity may be what raises us above the animals, but they also express in sound, and they build and construct. Projection needs to be studied. There is something unsatisfactory about a reality which exists largely on paper and ignores real life. The same objection can be made to the projection of the arts — they are no substitute for direct and waking experience. The mechanical or projecting method of passing information externally from one person to another must therefore be considered a limitation of the same order.

Objective knowledge is gathered from a minimum of sensory experience. Indeed experience, where possible, is replaced by measuring instruments. And the experience of the other senses all tend to be channelled into the single sense of the *eye*.

Modern science generally has accepted Galileo's distinction between matter and sensation (see p. 201), but his definition is not really satisfactory. It is insufficient simply to group *body* on one side of the Cartesian dualism, and both *thought* and *sensation* on the other. There is a major difference between sensation and thought, that has been ignored: Everybody has the *same* sensations, yet everybody has *different* thoughts — (this is if you like the 'difference' between them) — and that

244

is why modern science tacitly bases its definitions of reality on our sensations — such as our seeing a body move, or feeling its hardness. Ultimately any proof through evidence comes down to a sensation: when we look at the thermometer we all agree that the mercury has risen to 45; or when we look through the telescope we all agree that the moon has craters. It is because everybody has sensations in common that science calls our sensations *reality*. Any person can understand this reality, and shares it with everybody else. If one person does *not* hold a sensation in common with us we either convince him that his organs of sense are deficient, or else we say that he is 'hallucinated' or 'mad'. He is seeing something 'unreal'.

If you turn to Galileo's definition again on p. 201, you will realise that he is not really distinguishing between body and sensation, he is rejecting four of the senses and accepting evidence mainly from the fifth: his eyes — and partly his touch. It is very doubtful whether either Galileo or Descartes could have reached their idea about extension and the motion of bodies without their *eyes*. The only other sense that could convey this information would be the sense of touch — but touch alone, being a surface information, would probably not have reached such a description of body.

So although modern science relies on the senses, it tends to favour information from the sense of sight and touch: and ultimately, as it becomes more theoretical, it channels everything into the sense of sight. The history of modern thought is really the sense of touch being turned into sight by detachment. Even sound is explained in terms of vibrations. A sound is what we *hear;* but a vibration is what we *see* or *feel*.

This attempt to reduce the channels of information to one grid of experience is obviously done to unify and collate knowledge, and discard the misunderstandings and misinterpretation of extraneous 'thoughts' which confuse the evidence — each person having different thoughts. The fewer channels of information you have, the simpler your knowledge and the more easily shared.

This method of channelling suggests certain limits and alternatives. If you channel all information into one sense, you are clearly not using the other four in their full capacity, and you only have a *monistic* system. If you channel it into another sense you have another monistic system. But if you were to accept *two* channels as reality-finders you would have a *dualism*. And if you tried to discover a relation between these two without re-channelling them into each other, you would then have a *triple* structure — and so on. So if you accept all the five senses without re-channelling, you are likely to achieve a much more complex and interesting reality. The mainly modern method of having the sense of *sight* for our reality, and the sense of *sound* as our means of communication, presents a tacit confusion and is unsatisfactory.

We have evidence of other civilizations who have used the other senses to a higher degree. The ancient

Jews learnt a lot through sound — they did not just hear pleasant music and noise, they actually learnt facts, and heard commands and instructions. Conversely our sense of touch has been greatly abused by the Judaic-Christian civilization — they were expanding sight and sound over the other senses — but it may still have great importance. Probably yet other civilizations, like the animals themselves, have learnt a lot through smell and taste. Smell operates our strongest memories. If we combined senses without re-channelling them, we might, for example, find an experience-link between colour and taste, as in digestion; or between taste, smell and touch, as in asthma.

And this brings us to a new question. What is a *sense?* It is surely the reaction of our system to some external interference — a ray of light, a sound, a scent. But in *digestion* our system is reacting to food, and digesting it. Therefore we do not only have five senses — we may have many more. All our organs are potentially senses, though we have them at present in an 'unconscious' level of functioning — or an 'only conscious' (i.e. not objective) level. Our organs are certainly presenting us with reality and reaction; they may even be inducing *abstract ideas* rather than *sensory objects* in our mind.

So much for the Galilean restriction of objective knowledge to the sense of sight — and its possible extension into the other senses.

* * *

Now let us turn to the Newtonian reduction of all things, by increasing generality, towards a single cause or force that may be responsible for everything. This is the principle of Occam's razor and of Newton's own second Rule of Reasoning in Philosophy. It is implied in the great monistic philosophies of the Greeks, and of the Jewish single God who is all-in-all. And it is inherent in the scientists' assumption that no cause, law or explanation is sufficient until it has been shown to be universal, or universally applicable. This aim to reduce all phenomena to one single universal law or cause (of which other laws are merely fragments or sub-sections) has a good and sensible foundation. For if two different phenomena exist in the same universe, they must be connected in some way, and that very connection implies that they are contained within the same system and therefore subject to some common cause. It was this monistic aim that brought Newton to unite all terrestrial and celestial mechanics under one universal law of gravitation.

We see the same unifying and driving purpose in most science today. For example, Newton himself did independent work on the nature of light. But light seemed to be a somewhat different phenomen, and he was only able to hint a tenuous link between light and gravity. However, Einstein, by welding both gravity and light to space in a new way, was able to join them together and thus converted them into a *single* system, in true objective style.

The laws of electro-magnetism have now been discovered, and although these bear hints of a dualistic structure with their positive and negative charges (absent from gravity or light), there is hope that one day these laws too will be united with light and gravity to produce an even more universal and general law.

The same pattern appears in biological studies. Darwin established in the nineteenth century that all living beings are really only *one* animal that adapts itself to circumstances in its various parts and offspring. And as biology also bears traces of a dualistic system in cellular division and in the reaction of a living being to its surroundings, there is hope one day of explaining life in terms of chemistry and electricity, to produce a single unified system, whereby all life is chemistry and all chemistry is electricity. So here again objective thought is advancing along its favourite lines towards simplicity.

Tackling the subjective side of the Cartesian dualism has, of course, been a more trickly problem; but Freud, in true scientific and objective manner set himself to analysing the very thoughts and fantasies of the thinking 'I' as his *objects* of study — indeed he virtually turned them into objects, and propounded a system of psychology which is *universal* and common to all people, where almost the whole of human behaviour is said to proceed simply from an infantile reaction to *one* relationship: that of child to parents. Unfortunately this theory (if valid) cannot be joined with Darwinian or chemical theory because nobody yet knows how to cross over the

Cartesian dualism. But by this theft of our inner thoughts and desires, and projection of them forward almost as *objects* of medical study, the true subjective 'I' has been driven even further into isolation (or into a corner — if you look at it that way). Jung has complicated and improved this psychology by pointing out that the psyche has two compartments or units of operation — the ego and the Self. But he has also tried to redress the balance by pulling all our knowledge and experience back into the *subjective* personality.

Marx has followed a similar simplifying and objective method, in showing that all social behaviour and all social structure is due to human reaction of *one* type, to only *one* problem: namely class structure. Objective sociologists may one day hope to unite this with other sociological theories into a universal and single law of human behaviour — thereby spanning the gap between biology and zoology on the one hand, and between these and internal psychology on the other.

In short, the objective method has gone a long way to uniting the whole corpus of knowledge into three or four separate systems, and still has hopes of bridging the few hiatuses, and bringing all knowledge into *one* system — or as I would say, reducing it to only one thing. This, apart from being rather boring, would bring this method to its ultimate limit, as it would here have an end.

* * *

Apart from these few remaining hiatuses in our unified knowledge — such as the gravity/electricity hiatus and the Cartesian dualism — which may mark a barrier to objectivity, or perhaps show new points of expansion, there are also a few topics which are straining the *one-ness* of individual objective thought to its very limits. I will mention a few of them.

Newton himself led the way on one of these problems. It has generally been thought, on account of the uniformity and consistency of his mechanics, that Newton was a single-minded monist operating a *single-system System*. In fact he worked privately on other topics that we would class as lying on the other side of the Cartesian dualism. He worked for over twenty-five years on alchemy, using the medieval cosmic framework and attempting to discover the Philosopher's Stone. Since he failed here we can put this aside as a study in error. However, he also worked on the prophecies of *Daniel* and the *Apocalypse,* and seems to have calculated with remarkable accuracy the return of the Jews to Israel and other events in the twentieth century. His method of reasoning in prophecy has apparently nothing to do with gravity, unless he has hidden his link almost beyond recognition. In other words, Newton was operating with several independent systems of thought — alchemy, gravity, light, prophecy — to produce a *multiple-system System* of reality, or at best a dualistic system, even though he may ultimately have hoped to unite all his thought into one simple whole. We are on the threshold of the problem of *multiplicity,* which hangs over every monistic system like a cloud.

Another allied problem that stretches the limits of modern classical thought is that of the *universal* versus the *non-universal* event. Modern science has aimed to reach events which are both unique as regards time and space, yet universal as regards their laws of behaviour and everything else, in such a way that their uniqueness and and universality are synonymous and identified. So classical Newtonian physics rejects events which are simultaneously in several places (non-unique); or which are behaving according to their own particular and limited mould or law (non-universal). A non-universal event (if any such exist) would seem to challenge the very foundations of classical Newtonian objective reality.

A further problem straining the credibility of the single and simple objective reality is that of the co-existence of unrelated structures. For example, if there is such a thing as a non-mechanical event in biological affairs, how can this operate upon a body which is itself mechanically propelled? It other words, how can a non-mechanical event operate within a mechanical system, without automatically becoming mechanical, any more than I can kick a football with my will unless I mechanically push it with my foot? Thus if you have several layers or types of structure in the world each as a self-contained and closed system, how can they operate upon each other and coexist together in the same universe?

These then are some of the problems that stretch the powers of objectivity and monism. They point to definite limits in the possible reduction of all things to *one* only thing, or *one* only force or cause.

* * *

I have of course been deceiving you, and the aim of modern objectivity is not to reduce everything to one mind, one experience, and one thing. Its aim is simply to discover the truth, and here no holds are barred, no methods are rejected, if they help us to the truth; even though in recent years it has been found useful to correlate all knowledge into one mind, one experience, and one thing.

What then is this *truth* or *reality*, which modern thought is aiming to discover? Curiously enough reality means a different thing on each side of the Cartesian dualism. On the subjective side reality means freedom (though Buddhists would probably say that it means imprisonment). If I wish to move and find my way blocked by a door, I may learn to use the mechanism of the doorhandle, and opening the door, pass through it. My wish to move, the ground I walk over, and the door I pass through are all *real* and give me freedom — whether it be mental freedom, physical freedom, emotional freedom or any other kind of freedom. An insect that can see ultraviolet light, or feels amazing insect emotions, is involved in greater reality than we are. A madman who experiences greater freedom than we do is involved in greater *reality* than we are, though we call him mad.

But what then is waking up from a dream? Is it merely waking up to the greater physical freedom of the senses? It feels like waking into *reality*. So subjective reality may be something more than I have indicated.

On the objective or physical side of the Cartesian dualism, however, where the scientists are mainly working, the proof of reality or truth is *predictability*. So far as I can see, *predictability* is the only proof of reality or truth ever used by science. I know of no other. If two theories are presented explaining the same phenomena, that one which can predict the future of an event will always be chosen as the *true* explanation over the other, and will become the basis of our reality. The only slight preference we' have other than predictability is for consistency and simplicity. We preferred the Copernican over the Ptolemaic planetary system for this reason, even before there was any physical proof to confirm it. But these are only rule of hand preferences that can be discarded any day. So *predictability*, as I see it, is the touchstone of modern science and of objective *reality*. And reality has virtually no other objective meaning.

But what if predictability is discarded? How would we understand an extraordinary natural event that was unpredictable, unrepeated, or incomprehensible? We would tend to analyse it down to some recognisable parts and phenomena. In other words we would try to reduce it to its comprehensible and predictable parts, as a way of incorporating it into our body of knowledge.

254

So if we remove *predictability* we are once again on the very borderline of objectivity.

*   *   *

Having outlined the nature of modern individual objectivity, and run round its theoretical boundaries, we can watch its gradual disintegration during recent years, as mankind begins to step out beyond its limits.

Nobody but a fool would actually predict the future, and the seeds of a future cosmology are probably lying unnoticed in quite other spheres, but we can watch the shifts and disintegrations that have already occurred in our contemporary world. I will use again my five interlocking relationships as a guideline. We are concerned here with any discovery that changes one of the deep relationships, and thus probably indicates a change in all of them.

Once again the artists seem to be leading the way, at any rate as regards space. The recent explorations of the moon and the interplanetary rockets would suggest that the exploration of outer space is only just starting, and this may be so. But the artists are pointing elsewhere, and we can watch through them a gradual descent of the objective man, and the formulation of a new *man/object* relationship.

At the Cartesian dualism, which marked a break between 'myself' and 'other people', the individual conscious sentient 'I' was left stranded and isolated, facing a

255

reality that rejected him and all his personality. During the eighteenth and nineteenth centuries society worked increasingly towards a democratic ideal; but the artist's internal fantasy was more solitary than it had ever been. The novel flourished because it concerned social comment, and portrayed social life; and eighteenth century Rococo managed to keep in motion a flickering spirit of gaiety, now devoid of all social or deep realism. However, by the end of the eighteenth century, when the Romantic artist discarded the artificial Rococo gaiety of movement, he discovered that he himself was standing stock still. He found that he was standing alone as an objective person apart, alone on the shore, watching the flowing of Time, past present and future, as something from which he was utterly excluded. The Romantic artist became obsessed with Time.

The Middle Ages had experienced all time as a moving present in constant flux, and because they were living *in* it, they moved with it and were transformed with it. In the eighteenth century, already one step removed, Vico had hopefully tried to understand human history as a cyclical repetition of golden ages followed by decline. But for the early nineteenth century Romantic the cycle of time was already layed out in a long line, and there was no genuine return to the past, only nostalgia. The Romantic artist is the victim or cousin of the scientist; he stands on the bank like a detached observer, watching Time flow past him. He lives his life between complete immersion in unreasonable passion, and cold detached and unhappy criticism. He tries to plunge back into the river of life for a brief moment; and then steps back and idealises that instant of having really 'lived', recollecting his emotions in tranquility, and spinning his fantasy round them. It is the absence of this double vision that distinguishes the medieval mentality from our own. The Romantic is the artist trying to rejoin the mainstream of existence again and contact his own feelings, which the eighteenth century had so cruelly analysed away.

The late nineteenth century and Victorian sentiment that sweetens every feeling with excessive sugar, is probably really only the remains of sentimentality: a wish to comment on feelings while feeling hardly anything at all other than decorum and moral clichés. And twentieth century man has so completely inherited this vicarious attitude to his life, that he will spend his time devouring newspapers about other people's lives; and will sit for hours in a cinema or before his TV screen, to watch other people making love — not even other people, but the shadows of actors representing other people.

So the history of nineteenth century art reveals the detachment of the observer from reality in an acute form. Artists were trying to return to direct experience, and break down the barrier. And here the painters once again seem to have led the way. From the middle of the nineteenth century onwards painters began to abandon perspective vision — a sure sign that something deep was happening. First the Impressionist painters started to fill their canvas with daylight (a phenomenon almost unknown since the fifteenth century) and layed out their designs and landscapes in such flat areas of colour and sunshine as to minimise the perspective of a scene, creating vast impressions of vibration rather than any analysis of objects in space. Space has been replaced by light. Then Cezanne went further. He constructed a new type of space with multiple surfaces and no single viewpoint, as though viewing the scene as a series of flat planes. Mathematicians were concurrently beginning to construct systems of space with multiple dimensions. These spatial innovations of Cezanne were taken over by Braque and Picasso, and transferred to objects themselves. They invented Cubism, where a single viewpoint is rejected and every object is seen from many points of view either simultaneously or at different times and in different states. When this Cubist technique is fully pulled out it becomes like a film. And now, in fact, begins the early age of the cinema. So we are watching here a change in the *man/object* relationship.

A few years after Cezanne, and almost simultaneously, Einstein brought out a new cosmology where space and our knowledge of the world is also constructed on a multiplicity of view-points, producing a system of relativity. So here is the corresponding shift in the *man/cosmos* relationship. A few years later Dirac explained the the theory of the quantum jump — where a particle appears in one place and then in another, without actually moving to the other through the gap. This is a puzzle, but it sounds like a shift in the *cosmos/object* relationship, and may involve a new interpretation of the word space. Heisenberg's uncertainty principle makes yet another break in the classical structure of causality.

Since these recent discoveries seem to be naturally interlocked, we should I suppose be able to predict exactly what changes will soon occur in the other relationships. But prediction relies on 'change-within-no-change', and we cannot foresee the future. Interestingly enough the relation that has been hardest of change is the *object/object* relationship — perhaps because this relationship has been the main foundation on which classical modern realism was built. But I guess that when a deep change in the *object/object* relationship is eventually recognised it will so shake our opinion of what is real, that we will suddenly discover that reality has shifted, and we are in a new ethos altogether.

The general effect of these recent changes seems to be that man, the single objective observer, is diving down from his high place as God and acknowledging his place in the universe, recognising that he sees and knows things from within. In acknowledging his own viewpoint within the universe he is, in true objective style, increasing his objectivity.

But this diving inwards has also begun to occur on the subjective side of the Cartesian dualism. Instead of withdrawing the subjective 'I' further and further from the field of knowledge, thinkers have begun to stare into it. Those very painters who created Cubism began to shift from outer landscape towards internal fantasy, and

259

the dreams of the mind. German expressionism, Dadaism, Surrealism, were all engaged in this work. Artists have now followed this up with what looks like a total rejection of the *projective* method of the Renaissance. First they have refused to paint any figurative objects at all, thereby creating a school of abstract art; and lately they have even rejected the painted work itself as an art-object. They either smash open the frame, turn the painting into a piece of furniture, create something valueless that could never be sold as an art object, or else quite simply start working upon nature itself, upon anything on which they can lay their brush, spray or welding instrument. They are breaking down the barrier between the projected object of art and the real object: they say that everything is real and everything is fantasy. They seem to be smashing up the Cartesian dualism.

It is possible, of course, that we are watching here the decline of a visual art that has led the world of thought for several centuries. Perhaps music is now in the ascendant — feeding our spirit almost every hour of the day from every radio set. The sense of sound is free of place and independent of perspective, it comes from all directions simultaneously and has no back nor front. However, the visual artists are certainly still proceeding remarkably close to other thinkers.

The first great internal psychologists arrived on the scene simultaneously with the relativity theory of Einstein and the breakdown of the single perspective vision in art. Freud studied the fantasies, fears and actions of hysterical women, and thereby discovered or literally created a whole area of internal psychology. He began to analyse the motivations of the sentient 'I' rather as one might analyse the working of a clock or a living organ. Freud was working as a doctor and scientist, and still partly in an objective framework. But it was Jung, his disciple, who really broke the objective frame to pieces, and opened up a vast new field of potential. I must explain this a little more fully before we discuss Jung's theories.

We are observing a descent from objectivity in all the three pivots of classical objective thought: in the one mind, in the single experience and in the simple force. Any modification in these pivots is of fundamental importance. Einstein showed that our sense of sight has changed, and we must interpret differently what we see. Dirac and Heisenberg to a lesser extent tell us the same thing; but it is Jung who tells us that we can extend our minds to such an astounding extent as actually to alter, expand and completely transform our experience of reality.

Jung's fundamental theories are two-fold. He has pointed out that we have several types of consciousness or mental functions. He believes that we have two perceiving functions: *sensation* or perception through the senses; and *intuition* or non-sensory awareness. And we have two judging functions: *feeling*, or the capacity to judge with our feelings; and *thinking*, the capacity to order with our reasoning thought. Objective scientific

261

knowledge is almost exclusively built upon our thinking function. We may of course have many more conscious functions than the ones that Jung has listed, either unnoticed or still uncreated — such as plants or animals probably have. But Jung's theory is important because it widens our capacity to receive and understand new experiences. It fundamentally alters the powers and receptive abilities of the single objective thinker with his simple experience.

Jung's other fundamental theory is that of a *collective unconscious*. He explains that we not only have our own personal conscious and unconscious minds operating together and antithetically; we also all share in a *collective unconscious* that mostly reaches us in group experiences and images, which Jung calls *archetypes*. Although there is still no physical proof of the existence of Jung's collective unconscious (any more than there was for Copernicus' theory during many years), a phenomenon such as a collective unconscious would fundamentally alter the *man/man* relationship. Not only does it allow a communication between people which is no longer objective, detached nor through instruments, it also opens to our view new types of experience through new types of mind. We can now start to imagine a 2-mind or 3-mind consciousness that might be different from the single-mind system of individual objectivity. It's only a small step from this to sharing in the mentality of animals and plants, either by grafting or better by some collective unconscious link or sympathy.

262

Jung's theory thus envisages various *degrees* or levels of differentiation in consciousness, ranging from a collective unconscious, through archetypes, up to the most acutely objective individual awareness. So Jung has introduced the idea of an *undifferentiated* phenomenon in consciousness which is a total anomaly in our rigorously atomistic modern reality, though more akin to medieval thought.

Curiously enough neither Descartes, Freud nor Jung have said very much about consciousness itself. Descartes said nothing about the thinking 'I' — allowing all ideas to swim through it or be 'thought' by it freely. Freud, perhaps mistakenly, rendered it objective by turning it into an 'object'. He pictured it almost as an internal psychic structure in which a person moves about — a structure built from his desires and wishes and taboos. Jung pointed out that this psychic structure in fact consists of two rooms: We have a small area of ego-consciousness; but also a much greater structure which Jung calls the Self, and which relates to the archetypes and to the collective unconscious. However, all these are statements about the structure of the psyche. Neither Descartes, Freud nor Jung has said anything very much about the *act of awareness*.

This has been done more recently by Erich Neumann who has explained that there are two types of awareness, a focussed consciousness, and a matriarchal type of more diffuse awareness. If Newmann merely means that we receive some knowledge through unfamiliar channels

263

(and which therefore appear diffuse), it is not of any particular interest. But if this is really a *diffuse* phenomenon, it is a new concept of consciousness altogether, a new relation between man and reality, and forms a possible link between our individual focussed knowledge and a collective or undifferentiated unconscious.

So thinkers are gradually descending into the very misty area of the subjective 'I' which modern objectivity had so carefully discarded during the sixteenth and seventeenth centuries.

Perhaps in all these changes there are even vaster movings of the human mind, that take place over centuries or over mere minutes of time. Perhaps the Middle Ages, with great labour, managed to consolidate the formal heavenly world of light, only by rejecting the world of darkness. And perhaps modern classical objectivity from the sixteenth and seventeenth century onwards was able to incorporate into our knowledge this rejected world of physical darkness — only by putting aside and rejecting the subjective 'I'. And perhaps psychology is now beginning to incorporate the subjective 'I' into our field of knowledge — by rejecting or isolating some other phenomenon or experience which we still know nothing about and have no conception of — and so on, in vast sweeps down the ages.

Modern philosophers, curiously enough, have made a rather belated acknowledgment of the recent changes. The linguistic philosophers are still busy demonstrating that language is not logical nor objective — and as they are using logic to demonstrate it, they are having rather a rough time of it. More interesting perhaps is the school of 'existentialist' philosophers, because they challenge even the 'objective' structures of Freud and Jung. Aristotle had said that every organism has an *essence*, and its existence and behaviour follows from its essence. Thus an apple seed is in its essence an apple tree. This is in effect what Freud, Jung and other psychologists are also saying when they give the psyche a structure. But the existentialist philosophers assert, on the contrary, that man is free and he can exist and live as he likes; and only looking back afterwards will be discover what essence or being he has made out of his life. The existentialists assert that *existence* precedes *essence*, and man is therefore free.

But in opening these new problems I have reached the limit of this book which, although apparently studying five basic relationships between *man, object* and *cosmos*, has of course mainly been concerned with a sixth unlisted relationship between one cosmos and another cosmos: the relation between the medieval internal cosmos and the modern objective cosmos. For it is here, in the change-over from one cosmology to the other, that we have observed the gradual formation of modern objectivity.

ESTE LIBRO SE IMPRIMIO EN GRAFICAS EMA Y
LO ENCUADERNARON ALFONSO Y MIGUEL RAMOS
MADRID, NOVIEMBRE DE MCMLXXXII

15 - medieval world an internal division of totality

24 parallel structures and correspondences - of fractals.

58 - shift from internal to external

156 - objectivity and Protestantism ←

161 - capture of light by the individual

167 - 'points of view' the material of objectivity -

180 - maths and sorcery.

190 - for Kepler, space as Holy Spirit

195 - Leibniz saw gravity as an occult property of matter.

206 f - Descartes on extension

212 - Descartes on the past

214 - Descartes as thinking spirit

229 - Newton drove forces back to a point.

83 - use of neutral 'it' from C16

168 - man looking down like a god.

172 - space became still.

184 - perspective

189 - Kepler - change from circle to oval.

191 - gravity and levity.

/